Acknowledgements

This book is published by Enliven Press, for Didcot Writers.

The stories and poems in this anthology were selected by the editor from among the entries to Didcot Writers' summer competition 2019, which was themed 'museum'. Entrants were asked to consider –

What is on display behind the glass? Where did these things come from originally? Who works in the offices upstairs? What happens when the gallery doors close? What object of yours accidentally becomes an acquisition? What has been lost in the archive?

To find out about future opportunities for publication, local writing events, workshops, competitions, and everything else we do, visit **bit.ly/didcotwriters**.

You can also follow our activities on social media at **facebook.com/didcotwriters** and follow us on Twitter at **@didcotwriters**.

Museum Collection

an anthology of
short stories and poetry

edited by Alice Little

Contents

Prose

Poetry

Prose

A Winter-White World
by Rose Little

The Shattered Peace

As Abbie walked into the library of the museum, the quiet absorbed her and everyday cares vanished. Time seemed to be muffled here, like horses' hooves quietened by sanded roads. The clocks were both arrested at twenty five to eleven, just as her life for the last three years had been suspended in a kind of continual studenthood. She was aware of this and smiled to herself at being back in her chosen world after the family holiday.

There were a few people in the room, working in total silence: two or three students, an elderly woman with an engrossed expression who was photographing pages of a book with old leather bindings and tiny writing, a vicar peering at pictures of clergymen in a collection of newspaper cuttings. Abbie passed on to the librarians' counter and collected the box she had reserved. The box would contain the Literary Papers of the author, Daniel Kent, a cousin much removed, about whom she intended to write a biography. Twice a week she travelled to the university museum to which he had left his correspondence and literary papers, as he had been assistant curator there before going to work for a publisher. There was no indication that this day would change her whole view of her subject, cause a landslide in her mind.

Abbie had come to academic research late, as life up to now had focused on bringing up her children and writing romantic fiction, with which she had had some success and much satisfaction. However, academic friends she had kept in touch with from university had warned her about her style. 'Don't get confused and turn him into a romantic hero,' urged one. 'Sounds like you're falling in love with him,' said another. 'Aim for cool and detached.'

She sat down at the wide oak desk, setting out her laptop, pencil, notebook, magnifying glass and snake page-conserver. She opened the box reverently – this box had not been catalogued yet and it was a privilege to be the first to read its contents. It was obvious the curator hadn't examined them closely as the papers were in no kind of order. Abbie picked out a fat blue folder and laid it on the book support. On the first page was written *A Winter-White World*, the title of Daniel's landmark book. It would be interesting to read this, probably his first draft of the famous novel, and see what improvements he had introduced.

A Winter-White World had made his name, and in the 1950s and '60s he had gone on to write a dozen more novels. These had been interspersed with critical works, but for some reason no academic or student, no independent researcher had studied him, and now he had become hers. She felt the responsibility deeply and often looked at her one photograph of Daniel for encouragement. The young face looked back at her, fair-haired and handsome and still unformed. There was no trace of the sardonic wit that she enjoyed in his letters and his later books, but the kindliness was already there and the keen intelligence, in his direct gaze.

Now she touched the typescript of the groundbreaking novel and felt moved. She was surprised to notice that the title was written in a hand she did not know, perhaps a librarian's. She had read every word of Daniel's correspondence with the celebrated authors of his day and knew his handwriting to be like the man: direct, spiky, careful and correct, full of character – whereas this was a spidery, wandering hand.

Abbie flicked to the end of the 273 typewritten pages and started as an aerogram fell out. She opened it and began reading. Then she sat still and her heart seemed to stop beating.

'Dear Daniel,' it began, 'I am sending you under separate cover a little effort of mine, *A Winter-White World*. I would be very grateful if you could cast your critic's appraising eye over it and let me know if it will have any chance with your publishing house. Look after it as it's my only copy.'

The letter was in the same spidery, unsure hand. The

signature was simply 'Robin' so she turned back to the sender's address on the other side of the aerogram with its 6d stamp, postmarked 1955. 'Robin Forester, King George High School, Freetown', she read. *A Winter-White World* had been written by this Robin Forester.

There could be no doubt that Daniel had plagiarised the novel, the novel that had given him his start. Critics had pointed out how it differed from the rest of the oeuvre, but explained it away as his early, undeveloped style. Had he told Robin it was no good? Perhaps Robin had died soon after sending it to him and had never known of its success.

Aerograms from Africa

Rather abstractedly Abbie began to leaf through the next folder. It contained a jumble of aerograms waiting to be properly organised. They were all from Robin Forester. The writing was in the same wavering hand and difficult to read. Her eye fell on a few phrases from each as she glanced through them.

'A gloomy wet evening. I seem to be continually obsessed with the dangers and dreariness of life.'

'Picture me in my enormous house surrounded by my enormous garden of brilliant crimson poinsettias and dreadful animal life.'

'All night I am alone and all day I am waited on by servants including a chauffeur. Yes, I have a car! But there's nowhere to go, except into the rainforest all around. I don't feel comfortable having been given so much, but it is the custom here.'

'I am sunk in melancholy. Most of my friends have moved on, including the *sympathique* clergyman, and no one has replaced them yet. So there are no walks or tennis and definitely no real conversation.'

'At work I feel dull and lethargic and not likely to inspire anyone. There is no sunshine to cheer us up, the sky is usually overcast and looks sinister at this time of year.'

'It's been raining all day. I've just come back from an odd kind of Communion Service. An endless day lies ahead and an endless nine months till my next leave.'

'I was awfully cut up to hear you thought my novel was not real literature. I think you must have misunderstood what I was getting at. While on the subject, I must tell you that in the short story you sent me about the agnostic attending a service, you've got the number of candles wrong – it's a matter of church etiquette that is quite important.'

'I don't know why you should be surprised that I would like to take Holy Orders. The only reason I have not written to you with my thoughts in this direction is that I know your agnostic leanings would make it antipathetic to you.'

'I feel dreadfully isolated here, but it's by no means certain my job will continue and I may have to go somewhere even more remote.'

'The students are on strike again and if the new head of department doesn't arrive soon I will be in the firing line. It's safest to stay indoors.'

'I have had some trees cut down that were peering in my front windows. I expected to make the room lighter, but now a spectral whiteness pours in.'

'It's a still hot night, the rains have paused. I'm alone in my house – why don't I start writing a new novel, or shoot myself?'

A Dilemma

Abbie rapidly looked through the other papers – Daniel's notes in preparation for his critical works. She felt she must get away from the museum, oppressive to her now. There were no letters preserved from Daniel to Robin. A photograph of Daniel lay at the bottom of the box, his familiar face still handsome, only older, and for a moment she studied it in sorrow. All the humour and intellect were there, but perhaps there was some arrogance as well, some cruelty, that was absent in the earlier photograph.

Staring at the man Daniel had become she found to her dismay she could quite believe *this* man had stolen his friend's novel. She felt bewildered at Daniel's behaviour and then anguished on the unknown Robin's behalf: his loneliness and solitude had produced this sensitive book and he had never known how people would admire it – love it, even. Could he really have shot himself in his desolation?

If Abbie had paused beside the researching vicar she would have had the answer to her question, for from a faded photograph gazed the unworldly face of a new missionary, the Revd Robin Forester, being welcomed to a little township in British Guyana. But the knowledge that he had in fact survived Daniel was not to influence her decision.

Abbie handed in the box and walked out of the library. In her sleeve were concealed the title page and the aerogram, the only proof that the novel belonged to Robin. Seeking to raise Daniel's reputation she now possessed the means of destroying it, but exposing him would feel like a lover's treachery. The faces in the photographs rose before her, the young man she had been so interested in and the older man, running to seediness. She was angry with him but she could not quash the love she had felt during these years of study.

Leaving the building, she hurried down the main road, hardly noticing which way she went. She shredded the pages as she ran and pushed the pieces well down in a litter bin outside a cafe, then blindly turned homewards. The loss of her hero had drained all the colour from her life and she realised she had perhaps entered a winter-white world of her own. She would write Daniel's life story, but it would be colder now, more detached, as a true biography should be.

The Little Seaside Town
by Daren Carpmail

There wasn't much to do in this town apart from visit the museum, and I suppose that's why I became so fascinated by it. I've always loved the tawdry and the macabre, and this place definitely ticked those boxes. While I was staying in the seaside town I went there almost every day – it helped that it was only 5op to get in, and even that was a 'suggested donation'. I was often the only visitor, so God knows how they kept it going.

The town was no Blackpool or Brighton, you could hardly imagine tourists arriving by the bus load, but it was away from Michael, and that's all I really cared about.

*

I'd been looking for something, I suppose – aren't we all? I was just out of uni, doing a crap job and feeling like I was having a midlife crisis at twenty-two.

He was good looking, I'd give him that, and I couldn't deny being flattered when he started talking to me in the pub.

'Bit soulless, this place, isn't it?' He smiled at me across the bar.

'It's cheap, that's all I'm bothered about.'

'Hi, I'm Michael, let me buy you a drink.'

I wouldn't normally let a guy I'd just met buy me a drink, but he was lovely, and I was pissed off with my mate Laura. She'd just texted me to say she couldn't make it, leaving me in the pub by myself, prey to any dirty old man that might walk in.

I found him fascinating at first. 'Of course, I reject this kind of materialism,' he said, indicating the pub, which was hardly palatial. 'I see myself as a much more spiritual person, although I'm opposed to all forms of organised religion.'

'Oh, I know what you mean. I think that God is whatever we want him to be.' I leaned forwards. Yes, I was being flirty. With hindsight, I wondered why people like him always have a downer on organised religion. Should it be disorganised, or what?

'Most people don't get it, you see?' he said. 'They're brainwashed, they don't look into the soul and see that ultimately we are all energy. When we pass, our souls live on.'

I agreed. 'And, of course, everything happens for a reason.'

'Oh, you're so right.' He smiled, and what a smile it was.

We carried on talking bollocks like that for the rest of the evening, and we inevitably exchanged phone numbers.

Over the next few weeks the dates followed thick and fast. We ended up sleeping together on the third one

– very unusual for me. I'll be kind and say it wasn't exactly Olympic standard, but I've had worse, and he was certainly an interesting guy. We'd sit up all night smoking weed and putting the world to rights – usually by talking a load of New Age hippy shite.

'Your aura is looking good today.' He stroked my hair as I lay with my head on his lap.

'What?'

'Your aura. It's a lovely mauve shade. Usually it's an angrier red.'

I was a bit puzzled and I told him so, but he was unfazed. 'You see, love, I have more than the traditional five senses. I can perceive things that those with a closed mind cannot.'

'Oh,' I said. I think that was the first time I had any doubts about him. It wouldn't be the last.

*

The big row came on the day the new footie season started. Me and my dad are season ticket holders, and nothing and no one gets in the way of that.

'But, sweetheart,' he said. 'I really don't approve of competitive sports, and I don't want you taking part in something like this.'

'I'm not taking part. I'll be in the stands, munching on an overpriced hot dog and shouting at the ref.' I laughed, but he just looked pained.

'I'm sorry, I can't allow it,' said Michael.

'What do you mean, *allow?*' I was livid. 'You don't

allow me to do things? What I do or don't do is nothing to do with you.'

I stormed past him and went to the match.

We lost.

Afterwards, I went round to his house expecting an apology. His reply was unbelievable: 'I'm sorry Chloe, but I'm afraid I'm going to have to forbid you from seeing your father in the future. He clearly has a negative influence on you. I can tell by the state of your aura.'

'Forbid me? Who the hell do you think you are?' As I left I slammed the door in his stupid, sexist, hippy face.

The phone calls started the next day. He'd withhold his number and then hang up as soon as I answered, but I knew it was him. Then he started driving past my house at funny times. I wasn't afraid of him, not then, but I was sick and tired of his behaviour.

I returned from work a few days later to find my gate hanging off its post. When I went into the garden I couldn't stop screaming. My pet guinea pigs had been killed.

I called the police and they warned him off, but there wasn't much more they could do. He denied all knowledge, of course, though he admitted to the phone calls. He promised that he was over me and that he'd leave me alone in future.

I had a few weeks' holiday owing, so I decided to take

a break all by myself. I've always been happy in my own company, so I took the train to this weird little seaside town.

*

I went into the museum on my first afternoon. As I said, I love anything a bit weird, and this was definitely it. There was a bit about the town's history, not that there was much to say, really. Apparently The Who played there once, before they were famous, and there was a tour poster signed by Keith Moon. Other than that, there wasn't a great deal to see, not in the main part of the museum, anyway.

It was the waxworks at the back that really fascinated me. Trust me, it wasn't Madame Tussauds. For a start, I think their idea of celebrity ended sometime around 1998. Bobby Davro was there, and so was Samantha Fox. That one took plenty of wax, I would imagine. It's fair to say that they needed the name plaques underneath each one.

The so-called Chamber of Horrors was the best part. Not in the best taste perhaps, but I loved it. There was a room full of famous serial killers, ranging from Dr Crippen to Fred and Rose West. Again, they didn't look much like whoever they were supposed to be, but I was fascinated by them nevertheless. In dodgy wax, Myra Hindley was reunited with Ian Brady, and the Yorkshire Ripper was all set to rip again.

*

I was staring at the Ripper one day when I noticed something a bit odd. He was carrying a handbag, and not just any handbag either.

It was mine.

I blinked. Surely, I was imagining things? But I wasn't.

'Well, I can't imagine how that got in there, love,' said the warden as he unlocked the cabinet. He took a bunch of keys from a belt that was feeling the strain from his ample belly.

Sadly, I could imagine it all too well. As I walked back to my B&B I kept looking over my shoulder. A couple of times I thought I saw something out of the corner of my eye, but I'm sure I was imagining things.

Things calmed down for a few days until the death threats started. I don't want to go into detail, but they were vile. The notes were posted through the door, sometimes covered in blood or shit, and found by Greg and Hannah, the B&B owners. We told the police of course and they promised to keep an eye on things, but I know they can't be everywhere.

I was sitting in the dining room one evening, looking out at the dark garden through the net curtains and wondering whether I should call it quits and just head home, when there was a bang in the hallway: he had kicked the door down.

I jumped up as the lights went out. He grabbed me and put a knife to my throat.

'The old aura's not looking so good now sweetie, is it?'

'Better than yours, matey.' I kicked back, and hit him where it hurts.

As he writhed on the floor, I saw that the street was lit up blue. Someone had called the police.

He was arrested and taken into custody. The coppers assured me he wouldn't get bail.

The neighbour came over to help board up the door – he had witnessed everything, and Michael kicking the door down had been caught on his garage CCTV. This time I really was free of him. Sitting in the dining room at midnight, Greg and Hannah made me a cup of tea and reassured me that it was all over now. I was sorry they'd been dragged into it; I told them I'd pay for the door.

The next morning I went to the museum to say goodbye. I suppose I wanted to get a sense of familiarity before heading home to start my new, free life.

I noticed that since my last visit, they had put in a figure of Harold Shipman.

I looked closely. He was wearing my necklace.

The Marriage Curator
by Jane Andrews

My husband has always been highly organised.

As a child (so he's told me), he used to collect any letters he could find and throw them down the stairs into the 'sorting office' (aka the hallway), where he would spend a whole afternoon playing at 'sorting the mail'. Once he was a little older, it progressed to train spotting: he still has shelf upon shelf of tiny black notebooks, filled with neatly written numbers, along with dates and comments.

He's carried that precision over into our marital home: everything is neatly ordered, and each room has a different theme. Modern art adorns the walls of the 'Games and Entertainments Suite' (the living room); framed facsimiles of first edition Penguins decorate the book-lined 'Reading Room'; and the spare room is the haven for railway memorabilia: photos of trains, railway timetables and the ubiquitous spotter's notebooks. In the kitchen, mugs are classified not only according to 'His and Hers' but the type of beverage that has been deemed appropriate: try giving him a cup of tea in anything other than a railway mug, or a coffee in something that doesn't have a smiley face on it, and he'll refuse to drink it. The herbs and spices are all in identical jars with handwritten labels – in alphabetical order, naturally; and every utensil has a specific function – woe betide anyone who tries cooking vegetables in the potato pan, or vice versa.

Even our holidays are structured and ordered: we seem to have visited every museum – no matter how small or how bizarre – in the British Isles. Give him a room full of objects that have been listed and classified, and he'll be occupied for hours. In the past twenty years, we have visited the Postcard Museum on the Isle of Wight, the Pencil Museum in Keswick, the Dog Collar Museum at Leeds Castle, the Postal Museum in London (now updated into a slick tourist attraction) and the Pen Museum and Button Factory in Birmingham's Jewellery Quarter – as well as all the more traditional stately homes and places of historic interest.

It took me a while to realise that he has Asperger's. Although I'd read *The Curious Incident of the Dog in the Night-Time*, *The Rosie Project* and *The Colour of Bee Larkham's Murder*, these novels hadn't prepared me for the reality that those with ASD are characters who are endearing to read about but hell to live with. It's not just the compulsive chronicling of everyday minutiae that's annoying, but the lack of social connection. I sometimes think he'd pay me more attention if I had a number stamped across my face.

Now he's retired, he's even worse. He's taken over the spacious attic that used to be our son's bedroom –

since Adam's at university, his unused space is being filled with catalogued train timetables from the 1990s and every other current obsession. He won't let me look at whatever it is he's doing up there: the former attic has become a second storey 'man-cave', larger and more readily accessible than the shed at the bottom of the garden.

Our twenty-fifth wedding anniversary is approaching, but I'm wondering if I can be bothered anymore. Perhaps we'll be one of those couples who stayed together for the sake of the kids and then split up once they're no longer around. I'm certainly not holding any hopes of a romantic getaway or a special celebration – particularly when I hardly ever see him these days as he spends most of his time working on his 'project'.

For several weeks he has been more absent than usual, not hearing anything I say to him, barely communicating at mealtimes. If it were anyone else, I would assume he was having an affair; but John doesn't have time to conduct a clandestine romance: he's too busy ogling his back copies of *Railway Enthusiast*.

'Should I book somewhere for next Thursday?' I ask him loudly over the cornflakes one morning. He stares at me vacantly. 'For our anniversary meal,' I elucidate, adding, 'unless you've already organised something.'

The startled look on his face confirms my worst

suspicions.

I suppose I shouldn't let myself get too hung up about it – after all, John's never been one for romantic gestures. For our first Christmas together, he gave me a tin opener. At first, I thought it was a joke present, but then, as his eyes lit up, waiting for my reaction, I realised he thought I was as excited as he was. 'It's just like the one I had when I lived with Linda,' he said helpfully, referring to his ex-wife. By the time the Queen's Speech was finished, it had already found its way into the dustbin.

As our anniversary looms, he seems more reclusive than ever. He's now taken to disappearing for a whole day at a time, making himself a cheese and tomato sandwich and carrying it upstairs so he doesn't even need to come back down for lunch. He's stocked up with teabags and milk and the travel kettle. Occasionally, I hear his footfall as he descends to use the bathroom, but apart from that I don't see or hear him at all. It is as if our marriage has ceased to exist.

Despite the hurt I feel at being shut out of his life, I find myself going through the motions of buying a special card and even trawling Amazon to find him one of the missing volumes in his *Railway Detective* collection. 'Happy Anniversary!' I say, plonking the items down in front of him as he surfaces for breakfast.

John's suitably impressed with the card and gift, but there is a distinct lack of anything for me. 'Have you forgotten something?' I ask pointedly.

He makes a vague remark about having 'a surprise for me later', but I'm pretty sure he'll be dashing to the local garage for some wilted flowers later on.

It's only as he starts to disappear up the stairs to the attic that my anger explodes. 'For God's sake!' I yell. 'Can't you give it a rest on today of all days?'

He blinks at me uncomprehendingly. 'I just need to finish something off.'

I sit at the kitchen table, head in my hands, letting all the pent-up frustration of a quarter of a century drip out in tears I can no longer hold back. Surely it's not too much to expect just a tiny bit of romance once a year?

It must be an hour or two later when my errant husband reappears in the kitchen, where I am trying to drown my heartache by clearing out the cupboards. I wonder, momentarily, if he's just after more milk, but then he tugs at my sleeve. 'Come on, Margaret,' he says, his face bright with anticipation. 'I've got a surprise for you.'

Wordlessly, I follow him up two sets of stairs, wondering why I have suddenly been invited into his inner sanctum. He pushes the door open and the sight takes my breath away. Our attic room has become his Marriage Museum: every detail of our time together painstakingly arranged. Framed photos of the two of us line the walls, detailing our wedding, our honeymoon, our children. There is a wooden box on a stand, containing all our letters and cards to each other, and he's also displayed former gifts I haven't seen in years, along with more prosaic items. 'Is that my missing potato peeler?' I ask in surprise. When I asked him several months ago if he knew where it was, he replied with a non-committal grunt. At the time, I thought he wasn't listening; now I realise he had already earmarked it as a prize exhibit, being one of the first things he bought me during our courtship.

Lost for words, I survey the carefully curated display. His love for me is recorded in every exhibit. It's a shrine to our marriage – to us.

'Happy Anniversary,' he says, kissing me awkwardly.

And then I take him by the hand and we proceed to indulge in the sort of behaviour that definitely wouldn't be allowed in any other museum.

A New Agenda
by Alice Little

Professor Dale was drunk again. Simon could tell from the deliberate way he answered the phone, taking a breath between 'Hello, this is…' and 'the Museum of Historical Furniture' – as if he hadn't been sure whether to say his own name or that of the institution.

'Dr Marsh,' the professor called to Simon across the office, snapping his fingers and pointing at the door.

Intuiting his boss' meaning (as he did every day), Simon went to open the door to the gallery, finding on the other side a dishevelled man in his late twenties, perhaps a few years younger than himself. He was, thought Simon, the most beautiful man he'd ever seen, though his hair stood up over his ears and his clothes were wet from the rain. He held a mobile phone.

Giving Simon an apologetic smile, he walked into the room. 'Sorry, Dad, couldn't remember which door was yours.'

Simon smiled at his insecurity: there were only two doors. He was clearly intimidated by the austere surroundings of the gallery.

'Nathan, this is my assistant, Dr Marsh.'

Simon held out his hand and gave his first name. He didn't correct the professor as he usually would: being

Assistant Curator was not the same as being a Curatorial Assistant or PA to the Curator.

'How do you do?' said Nathan, lingering long enough over their handshake to give Simon hope.

Simon returned to his desk and looked again at his catalogue – documentation bored him to tears, and he found it far more engaging to watch Nathan over the top of his monitor and wonder how he could engineer a private chat.

'Dr Marsh, would you mind showing my son where to find the archive? I need to get to my lecture.'

Perfect.

Professor Dale's lectures were not what they had once been. He had come to the Museum of Historical Furniture from an auction house, where he had become an expert in eighteenth-century sideboards. He could authenticate a Chippendale at thirty paces.

But since his wife's death he had become cynical, turning up on time but often snoozing at his desk, attending administrative meetings but returning to the office and ceremoniously burning the agenda in the sink using an antique lighter he kept on his desk for the purpose. Simon knew the professor was coasting to retirement but, at sixty, that was still half a decade off and by that time Simon would certainly have been expected to have taken up a curatorial post elsewhere. He'd already been approached by a contact in Glasgow, but Glasgow wasn't Oxford, and it was a long way away.

'So, what's it like working with my dad?'

Simon was glad Nathan had said 'with' and not 'for'.

Nathan held the door open for him at the end of the corridor. As he passed, Simon smelled cigarette smoke on Nathan's clothes. That was a negative point, he thought, but he reckoned he could live with it.

'I enjoy working in the museum,' he replied, neatly avoiding Nathan's actual question. 'My specialism is Queen Anne bedroom suites, so it's wonderful to be in the same department as an authority like the professor.

'Right.'

Oh god, he'd sounded too diplomatic and grovelling. Simon needed to lighten the tone. 'I bet you grew up surrounded by Rococo twists and turned table legs. What do you do?'

'I'm a carpenter,' Nathan said. Simon quelled a strong desire to look down at Nathan's hands. 'I'm more practical than Dad – the beauty for me is in how you achieve the effect and execute a design, rather than the important thing being that the work was done by someone who's no longer alive.'

'Maybe one day we'll have some of your work in the museum.' He laughed at himself and added, 'Hopefully while you're still alive.' If only Simon were responsible for accessions, the collection would have updated its focus and begun to commission new works years ago.

Nathan smiled. 'I'm considering moving into restoration, actually. That's why I'm here: Dad said I could look up the old catalogues and conservation records, that sort of thing. Because when you try to make something better, you need to choose whether to take it back to how it was originally, or whether to honour the changes that have been made since.'

Simon had to make his move now, they were nearing the door to the archive. 'Interesting,' he said, 'I'd love to hear more about your ideas.' *Was it enough?*

'I'm sure I'll have plenty of questions once I've spent a few days looking at documents: paperwork isn't really my strong suit.'

Simon took courage from the reply, and they parted at the entrance to the stores where the archivist took over, and Simon returned to his office.

Back at his desk he found an email from his contact at Delaney's, an auction house that had taken on the sale of furniture from Raynor Lodge, after the death of the owner.

'I thought you were set on the wardrobe? – but an anonymous account bid uncontested and it's gone now.'

Simon's heart thudded. Professor Dale had been responsible for getting the Museum's bid in on time. This had been his once in a lifetime opportunity to acquire such an object – it would have brought the world (or at least the world of furniture design) to their door. Simon could have developed his own research and written his second book, using the wardrobe as his central case study. Now the opportunity was lost.

He sat at his desk, staring at the screen without focusing. He felt bereft. A tear rolled down his cheek and he wiped it away, torn between grief and anger.

It was the final straw, thought Simon. He turned off his computer, his hand shaking slightly. He was off on annual leave for a week starting tomorrow: he'd leave early and consider his next move. Maybe he should get in touch with his contact in Glasgow after all.

Simon's week away was dominated by these thoughts. In an ideal world, Professor Dale would be retiring at the end of the year, and Simon would be appointed to replace him. He was the natural successor, after all, and he knew the Museum would prefer that to an extensive and expensive recruitment and training process.

If only there was a good way to expose the professor's decline into incompetence without tarnishing the museum's reputation. Perhaps an important armchair might be broken or a collection of tools lost? But he risked such a calamity being merely overlooked: things went missing all the time – they usually turned up, so it wasn't news; and the museum's conservation department was excellent, so a mere breakage wasn't much of a threat. Or, worse, responsibility might be laid on him and he, as the junior member of the team, would be forced to leave in disgrace.

No, he needed to think of something that would lead the professor to accept early retirement, and ensure his own job would be secure. And things would have to be pretty uncomfortable for Professor Dale to consider leaving the museum before his time.

Fire. That would do it.

Enough fire that the professor wouldn't want to stay, but not enough to damage the cream of the collection. A fire in the office perhaps, starting where the professor burned his paperwork. The investigation would reveal the professor's unsafe habit (via Simon himself, if no one else remembered it first) and he would be encouraged to leave. Simon would then step into the breach and manage the recovery of data and reconstruction of the records. And if any items in the collection were damaged he might be able to get Nathan the contract to restore them.

Simon daydreamed all the details while he was away, not quite believing he would ever follow through on such a plan. But then on the last day of his holiday he found himself checking out of his hotel and not leaving his luggage for the day as he had planned, but instead getting straight back in his car and heading for the museum. He arrived at a time when he knew the professor would be out, and tailgated a visitor through the staff entrance so his swipe card wouldn't give him away.

The ashes from Professor Dale's last agenda were still in the sink. Cold, of course, but not wet. If a tea towel had fallen into the sink just after the professor had left the room, Simon wondered, would it have caught fire? Taking a wodge of paper from the printer and covering his hand with his sleeve to use the professor's lighter, Simon set the pages alight, then casually flicked the tea towel off its hook.

Yes, it would have caught fire.

Simon trailed the end of the tea towel onto the bookshelf, and pushed some loose papers towards it. Then he left the building.

He had a call from the administrator just after ten that evening: '…wanted you to know before you come back… sorry to have spoiled your holiday… the fire brigade are making it safe, the building will be off-limits until Monday.'

On Monday morning the professor met him at the gate, sober. 'A sorry mess,' he said, manoeuvring past a large crate in the gallery and lifting the police tape for Simon to go into the office. 'And on the day your beloved wardrobe arrived too – I'd hoped to have it out of the box by the time you got here.'

Simon stopped walking, stunned.

'It was a silly idea, really, but I wanted it to be a surprise. I put in a bid myself, and will be donating it to the Museum. It was to be a sort of leaving present.'

'A leaving present, Professor?' Simon's throat was dry.

'Yes, I was planning early retirement. But that's all been cancelled now, they need me to stay and sort all this out.'

Simon began to sweat. 'And do they know what happened? How it started, I mean.'

'Ah, now, that is a little embarrassing,' Professor Dale said. 'I was home ill on Friday.'

Simon's blood ran cold. The professor wasn't in on Friday. The ashes in the sink must have been from the day before, why hadn't he thought to check the professor was at his lecture?

'Why is that embarrassing, Professor? We all need time off sometimes.' Simon was still mentally kicking himself.

'Well, you see, I gave my keys to Nathan so he could come in and look some things up.'

For the second time that morning Simon felt his heart skip a beat.

'He told me last night, he was smoking while he worked. Stupid boy. The police came round first thing this morning to question him. He'll have to face the consequences.'

Simon nodded mutely.

'Now, shall we take a look at this wardrobe of yours? That'll cheer us up a bit, won't it, Dr Marsh?'

Axe Head
by David Lewis Pogson

The axe head was very familiar; Sam had seen it in use. He was seeing it again now, centuries later.

His back was aching and he wanted to sleep. He'd known that this trip to the British Museum would sap all his energy. His condition often made him tired.

The sheer number of exhibits and the detailed display cards he'd been reading had made the time drag. He had to read them all to check their accuracy, making notes of where the experts had got it wrong. They were forced to speculate because they didn't have memory to draw upon.

He'd corrected the display labels in a general way in other sections of the museum for more recent periods in history but, for him, this special exhibition in Room 50 (Britain and Europe 800 BC–AD 43) had a direct personal connection. He sat down on a marble bench at the side of the gallery, leaning against the wall, clutching his rucksack. Then he stretched his legs along the slab and closed his eyes. So far, this was the furthest back that he'd tried to remember. And it had been exciting, taking a lot of his energy to manage it.

The artefacts were from a dig near his home town – the discovery of a complete village. These artefacts were the reason he'd made this latest trip to London.

The dig had been undertaken in strict secrecy, to guard against looters, so he hadn't heard about it until it was all over, otherwise he would have volunteered to help.

It was more than a feeling. From what he'd read he'd been as sure as he could be that these were artefacts used by his direct ancestors. In particular, he'd been transfixed by the corroded axe head and the remains of its wooden shaft and bindings, preserved in its wrappings by the bog acid, and now displayed in the centre-aisle cabinet. He recognised its distinctive shape. He could recall its original polish, its weight, its balance. But the effort of regressing and recalling it in all its detail had made him drowsy.

He was well aware that his inherited memory was unique: who else could remember the detailed life of preceding generations in their male lineage? Despite rapid scientific advances, DNA was still very much a mystery yet to be fully unravelled. No one had discovered the gene that allowed his brain to work in this way. But then, how would they know to look for it? No one else that he was aware of, including those in his family, had ever claimed to have such an ability. Sometimes he watched those idiots who subjected themselves to hypnotic regression on television shows claiming to recall past lives, but no one took that seriously. This was the nearest anyone had come to having his ability, but their subconscious minds could be manufacturing fake identities. Whereas he had tested his memory against every age in every museum he could visit. Familiar objects – tools, weapons, clothing, jewellery, coins and pottery – all acted as triggers. Today, the axe head had kicked it off. Nothing had ever been as familiar as that: not until he had seen the bodies.

*

He remembered telling the village elders what happened.

We were out of sight of the village, cutting peat. I'd been sent to fetch water for them. Olaf had a new axe, polished and shaped perfectly. Sizing the turf required skill. His brother Bradan had no axe. He lacked the strength for sustained cutting. His purpose was to stack the turf and help carry it back to the village. His was a menial job.

Everyone knew that the women of the village wanted Olaf, wishing they could lie with him. The women rejected Bradan whenever he tried. His hunched back put them off. He had to sleep near us. At night I could sense him listening, from our side of the hut, to the sounds of Olaf taking pleasure with the one he'd chosen for the night.

Olaf put down his axe and turned to pass the fresh cuts. Bradan picked the axe up, testing the balance, thinking they were alone. I knew he'd admired that axe before. Then he struck the blow. I dropped the water pot, it shattered and I ran back to the village.

*

He awoke to the sound of a London Walks tour guide addressing a party of Japanese teenagers. Their cameras captured every artefact.

'The items in this cabinet came from a very interesting excavation at the edge of a peat bog. Ancient Britons lived near the bog in Iron Age dwellings. They used ore deposits to create artefacts like that axe head. They smelted the ore in clay furnaces, before beating and shaping it over hot fires. But–' he paused for dramatic effect '–we haven't solved the mystery of the two graves on the other side of the hill, so well preserved by the peat.

'One contained the body of a tall well-built man of high status, judging from his clothes and his grave goods including that axe head. He died from a savage chopping blow to the back of his skull – a penetrating head injury as they say in forensics – which damaged the skull and undoubtedly caused an immediate fatality.

'The other grave contained the body of a shorter man, his back hunched from a genetic spinal deformity, and with his arms tied behind him, his feet bound, lying face down with a ligature tight around his neck. A man of lower status, completely lacking in grave goods. Were they sacrificed or simply caught out of sight of the settlement by passing marauders? We may never know.'

Sam sat up and stretched as the tour group moved

around the cabinet, phone-cameras clicking.

The ache in his back was worse from slumping. He'd been the only one affected by the deformity in his immediate family, although he knew that others before him either carried the defective gene or suffered from it. He'd tried improving his posture through exercise, and even had steel implants to straighten his spine, which had improved things, but it still caused him pain when he spent too long on his feet – especially today, when he'd stooped over the cabinets studying the exhibits in detail through the glass. The doctors told him it could skip generations and that not all siblings would share the deformity. He was just the unlucky one in his family this time.

The tour guide continued speaking. 'What is interesting is that the museum is proposing to carry out DNA research using the national database. Since compulsory registration was introduced fifteen years ago the entire population has been tested and recorded, so now it might be possible to establish if these bodies have any descendants living today.'

Sam didn't need a DNA test to tell him that the bodies he'd been viewing, on display in the airtight glass cases nearby, were related to him – one in particular.

Despite the black pigmentation from the peat and the distortions from the packed soil of the burial, the natural decay and ageing had been held at bay, preserving the bodies, and their clothing and possessions, almost as they were when buried. It was like looking at himself in an earlier age, or at least at an ancestor whose life he could recall in vivid detail. It was a strange and emotional experience. It had never happened before in any of the other ages. Either the bodies were lost in time or buried in official graves never to be disturbed.

He would take part in the DNA test. It would be further proof of his memory when the link to these bodies was established for certain. Possibilities that had lain dormant now revived in his mind. Soon it would be time to reveal his unique ability; maybe write a book, become a celebrity, sell the film rights. There would be lots of media opportunities to take advantage of. It could make his life easier. Maybe a little bit of wealth might make him attractive to women.

He followed the Japanese tourists back to the cabinets to take a second look at the bodies.

'It's possible that the museum artists will be able to sculpt replica faces based on the preserved flesh and bone structure of the two bodies.'

That could help his claim too. Who would play Olaf's part in the film? Someone tall and handsome and strong. Sam could picture it now. And Olaf's brother would be played by someone small and bent. A man that no woman would ever lie with. Indeed, no woman had ever lain with his uncle: he'd had no opportunity to father children before they'd executed him. His testimony had ensured that.

He looked at Olaf's head injury. It had been a quick death. It had been the best axe he'd ever held. He'd placed it in his father's grave.

Pears

by Lee Shupe

'It was you, wasn't it?' Silence on the other end of the line.

Lucille Montevideo manages to hold her cell phone to her ear and keep her purse perched delicately on the same shoulder, the weight of her laptop case throwing the whole waddle from the car to the back door of her café into question. 'Colleen? Colleen, is that you?'

Straining against sobs: 'A guard was murdered… please tell me, Lucy, that you didn't rob the Guggenheim?'

'Colleen, I don't… I don't know what you're talking about. Are you OK? Is everything all right?'

Colleen ignores the question but Lucy doesn't hear what she is saying, as she fishes out her key, straining to see why the place appears vacant.

The lights are off in the kitchen. Forgetting to end the call, Lucy puts her things down on a counter and shuffles into the dining room, hands on hips, squinting as if it would help explain the deserted café.

'Hello Lucille.' Lucy jumps. The words come from a man sitting at a corner table holding a newspaper. He doesn't even look up. 'I didn't mean to frighten you.'

The man stands. She sees a red leather gun holster

peeking out from under his tan corduroy blazer. 'I sent everybody home. Customers, your staff. I figured we needed to talk, but you are far too busy. So,' he continues offhandedly, 'I cleared your schedule.'

'I suppose you're going to tell me who you are at some point.' Lucy remains standing, as if expecting a quick answer. In her mind she pictures the man's head on a rat's body and she is sweeping him out of the little cottage café.

'Agent Henshaw, FBI.' He eyes the blown glass animals displayed on a few shelves by the front door. 'Looks like you collect small jewelled objects, Ms Montevideo. I bet jewelled pears would make a grand edition to your little collection here.'

Lucille interrupts. 'Look. First of all, those are blown glass, not jewels. Second, I don't know what you're referring to, but–' she pauses, the guilt of spending fifteen years of her young life plotting to steal the pears weighing heavy '–I'm definitely going to call the police if you don't leave.'

'Oh, I'll leave, Ms Montevideo, but I'll be around town and I'll be in touch.' He turns the 'open' sign back around on the front door, unlocks it, and exits. 'Have a good afternoon.'

Lucy returns to the counter by the back door where she left her belongings, regretting what she has done, the gravity of it dragging down her stomach like it's tethered to a millstone. When she looks at the back window, she freezes. The jewelled pears, which she had hung as a sun catcher to disguise them, are gone – ripped from the fishing line that held them, its frayed knot catching little bits of the afternoon sun instead.

She ignores the small voice from the phone. 'Lucy? Lucy? Are you still there?'

This and That
by Georgina Richardson

Toni's been to the local history museum once a week for the past fifty-three weeks. Last week was the anniversary so Trevor had the whole day off work to be with his wife. Neither of them knew what they were meant to do so they ended up sitting at home in silence for the majority of the day and not even in the same room as each other. Toni has grown used to the silence. It's a stillness in the air, one where every scrape of a fork against a plate or flick of a light switch is intensified. Then in the late afternoon, Toni had snuck out. Trevor probably hadn't even noticed she was gone. He's stopped bothering to ask her what she does with her days or he's stopped listening if she does bother to say.

Today she goes back to Warley Park and loiters outside the museum. It's mainly the families she watches, some with one parent, some with two, as they come back out or go inside together. Sometimes the parents look harried. Sometimes they look devastatingly happy. Sometimes they just look bored and this alarms Toni the most. Eventually she walks up the fourteen stone steps and goes through the automatic doors. She doesn't dare make eye contact with the man on the reception desk. From afar she sees that he's new so he probably won't recognise her. Aware an entrance ticket isn't required, she walks straight past him and heads towards the galleries.

'Ma'am, excuse me. There's a bag search before you go in,' says another man in one of the pale blue polo shirts the museum staff all wear. Toni doesn't recognise him either. His name badge says *Craig – Security Team*. This is new. Unexpected. Reluctantly, and a little shaken up, she hands him her oversized handbag.

'Can you unzip it?' he asks. His authoritative voice sounds too stern. This stony stranger demanding to look at her belongings also insists that she be the one to reveal the contents of her bag. Obediently – for what choice does she have? – she opens it up. The man peers inside using a slim torch. There are sanitary towels, a large plastic keyring with picture of Eithan, a deodorant stick as she's always sweating these days, her car keys, and remnants from days that are now gone: baby wipes, plasters with pictures of dinosaurs on, a small cardboard box of sultanas that's been squashed up, and a few pieces of Lego that Toni hadn't even realised were there.

'That's fine,' he says, already looking towards the next person.

The first gallery is the smallest and is dedicated to prehistoric times. In one corner, there's an Iron Age roundhouse. Today two little girls are sitting inside playing with the pretend fire. If she blinks, Toni can see Eithan sitting inside dressed up in one of the costumes. He'd nag her to go in with him and play, but Toni would be preoccupied trying to get the perfect photo of him to show Trevor that evening how much fun they were having. She's read all the information boards now. Back then she never bothered. She'd be able to tell Eithan now that the walls and roof were made from wattle and daub.

The second gallery is a popular one. It was Eithan's favourite. There are lots of things to play with. It's supposed to be telling the story of trade and industry in the area but most children don't bother to read the accompanying information. It always amused Toni at the time that Eithan most loved dressing up as a butcher and bagging up plastic steaks and sausages. They were a strictly vegetarian family, on ethical grounds. Toni suspected that Trevor had long been flouting this when he was out of the house. Toni had also mindlessly lapsed a number of times. There's a chubby preschooler behind the butcher's counter today. If she could, Toni would go back and take Eithan to a real butcher's shop and let him choose whatever he wanted.

Toni walks quickly through the next gallery with all the stuffed animals. She knows the names of all the different types of ducks now. Before, she would have just called them ducks. There's something truly awful about a dimly lit room housing hundreds of stuffed, dead animals. It reminds her of a mausoleum she and Trevor once visited in Italy. It had been well reviewed on TripAdvisor but when they'd actually got inside Toni had felt ashamed and empty.

At the far end of the room, there's a telescope. It points out the window towards a shaded corner of the park with little in it, so there's hardly ever anything to see. Eithan would always want to have a go on it though. Even if she has to wait for someone else to finish, Toni now always takes a look through, every week. It looks darker outside than it was before she came into the museum. As usual, she can't find anything worth looking at.

'Here again?'

Toni turns around, uncertain whether the question or statement is directed at her. Then she sees a young woman she feels is vaguely familiar.

'Do I know you from somewhere?' Toni asks, searching the woman's face for a clue.

'Chelsea Maddington,' she says, looking away.

'I remember,' Toni tells her as it comes back to her. It's an unusual name. She's dyed her hair red, it looks like a henna wash, and her clothes are different. She's older, of course. 'I taught you – it must have been five or six years ago.'

'Five years ago,' Chelsea confirms.

Toni's aware that it's her turn to speak but they both

stand in silence for a while. Finally, she asks, 'Do you want to get a drink?'

Upstairs in the museum's cafe, they sit opposite one another at one of the ugly aluminium tables. Chelsea has a slice of carrot cake and a mug of tea. Toni sips sparkling water, which she doesn't even like. She punishes herself in small ways as much as possible.

'So, what are you doing these days?' Toni asks. She guesses Chelsea's probably at university now. Perhaps she's studying art or something like that – she seems that type.

Chelsea takes another large bite of her cake before answering, 'I work in admin. I'm at the county council at the moment but I don't know how long it'll last.'

'Why's that?'

'Who knows,' she says as she continues eating the cake at a rate that's almost impolite. She looks too skinny.

'What happened to your mother?'

'Are you still a teacher?' Chelsea asks, looking up from her empty plate. Toni thinks for a moment that she might be about to lick it like a cat. 'I heard about your son,' she adds, speaking too quickly, 'I saw on the news.'

'I don't teach anymore,' Toni explains, 'I stopped when Eithan was born.'

'You were a good teacher.'

'Well…' Toni begins, about to list the reasons why

she hadn't been a good teacher, but then she changes course. 'Have you seen me here before? You said about me being here again.'

'I come here quite often. On my days off or whenever I can really. I've seen you a few times. You must come a lot too.'

'It's the last place we brought Eithan. We'd been here that afternoon just before it happened.' Toni stalls as she speaks. It's the first time she's talked about the accident in a long time. Chelsea listens without interrupting. She doesn't say anything insincere or insensitive, or anything at all. She just listens.

Then she tells her own story and Toni listens.

They finish their drinks and then walk around the temporary exhibition rooms which are also upstairs. There's an exhibit about robots which Eithan would have loved. They'd probably have made up stories and given each robot a personality. He'd have drawn them when they got home.

'So, I guess I come here for the same reason as you,' Chelsea says as they stand in the foyer downstairs.

They walk out of the museum together. Neither of them drive: Chelsea can't afford to and Toni just can't.

The following week they meet there again. It becomes a regular thing. The mother without a child and the grown child without a mother. Every week they walk through the galleries and Eithan and Penny come back to life for them. It's natural when they're in the galleries to say *Eithan loved this* or *Mum liked that*. They always meet at the museum. Neither of them ever suggests meeting anywhere else.

The Museum of Lost Dreams
by Noa Covo

The museum of lost dreams awed me now just as much as it had when I was a child.

When I was little my father would take me there with him, through the forest that began in our backyard. He would walk bent with his hands stuffed in his pockets as I dragged a plastic bucket full of rags behind me, struggling to catch up. The bucket was heavy, but every time my arms felt close to giving out, the museum would appear.

'We're here,' my father would say, even though there was no way to mistake the white building that seemed to grow out of the ground the same way the trees did.

I would fill the bucket with water from the hose outside while my father fished the key from his pocket. When I had dragged the bucket back, he would still be holding the key in his hand, staring at the locked white door. Holding the key now, nearly twenty years later, I found it was a normal size, but when my father held it in his open palm all those years ago, it seemed like the heaviest thing in the world.

This was the first time I had been here alone, and the first time I'd ever unlocked the door. It swung open noiselessly. It was cold inside, just as it had always been. I put the key back in my pocket and picked up the bucket before taking a step inside.

As a girl, I'd always wondered where the light came from. My father never turned any lights on or off. There were no windows inside the Museum of Lost Dreams, and yet there was light, in parts harsh and forbidding and in others dim and melancholy.

I had forgotten how long the room was. An endless row of glass displays, gleaming softly, full of hopes, full of fears. The first time I asked about it, questioned it, my father hugged me tightly.

'These are things our family wanted,' he said gravely. 'Things they wanted, but could never have. This is a museum of lost dreams.'

When I was older, I learned another thing this place was: a secret. My friends weren't to know. Nor my grandparents. When my mother came to visit from distant South Africa, she wasn't to know, either. It was as if the museum were a chasm, a barrier between my house on the edge of the forest and the world I wanted to be part of – the chasm that at eighteen, I would immediately scramble across, leaving my father behind.

'Why do we have to clean it?' I'd asked, then.

'To remember,' my father said, dipping a rag in the bucket, and that was that.

His words still echoed around the hall twenty years later as I began to clean. The glass was streaked with dust – my father hadn't been able to come here in a long time. I thought of the version of him I saw this morning tottering down the stairs. He was dying, his legs shrivelling up along with the rest of him.

'Is there anything I can do to help?' I had asked at breakfast. I had arrived the day before, with a suitcase full to bursting with clothes and emotions. The last time I had been in the house was a week after my eighteenth birthday. Everything felt foreign, like watching a movie I knew well in a language I didn't speak. My father smiled as he slowly spooned oatmeal into his mouth, and whispered his request. I was to go to the museum. There was no mention of the bucket, but I brought it along anyway.

The museum held everyone's lost dreams. My great great grandfather married the wrong woman; the woman he lost was displayed behind the glass, rosy cheeked and happy. There was a great aunt who lost her chance to be a painter, a grandfather who had always wanted to travel. Lost, wasted, stuck behind glass that I scrubbed. When I was little, I wanted to hear every story. I'd press my nose to the freshly cleaned glass and my father would tell me, with precision.

'How do you remember all this stuff?' I asked him once. There were no plaques. No way of knowing. Just an endless concrete corridor.

'I have to,' my father said, and pushed a wet rag into my tiny fist.

'Did you come here with grandpa?' I continued as I scrubbed yet another pane. I never knew how long we spent inside the museum. Sometimes it seemed like minutes, other times like days.

'A long time ago,' he said.

There was a child in the next display case, a child that someone would have had but never did. His eyes were as big and surprised as my father's were yesterday when I showed up on the porch of my childhood home – we hadn't spoken since I left.

'I heard you were sick,' I said before biting my tongue. He was crumpled up so small I was surprised the wind hadn't taken him. I tried to hide my shock by raising an eyebrow at his plaid pajamas.

'I didn't know you were coming,' he replied. He had no reason to.

I scrubbed the glass hard now, thinking of how long it had taken me to show up on the porch. I had convinced myself I was all grown up after leaving home, but teenage me was still very much alive, the same teenager that let her father carry the blue plastic bucket into the woods by himself, not caring that he would be alone in that great white building. His museum of lost dreams was boring, and weird, and it had nothing to do with me.

My fingers lingered on my grandmother's lost dream to be a pilot. I'd loved hearing about that dream. Every time we were here Dad would tell it, until the day I decided I wasn't interested anymore, four years before I moved out without even a goodbye.

My arms were tired, and I stopped cleaning for a moment, staring at the glass ahead of me before realising that in front of me was a new display.

My father always told me the museum made the displays appear, that all he did was keep them presentable. I'd never really believed him – but the case in front of me must be the reason he had told me to come here. It was so new, the glass was still crystal clear. No one had ever smudged it. Inside was a calendar.

I pressed my nose to the glass. It was a calendar that spanned years, with months in little boxes, just like the one on my father's fridge. I had one in my dorm room. Many of the days were crossed out in red ink. The first month in red was a month after my eighteenth birthday. The last one was the day before I got on a flight home. Missed months added up to missed years, in which neither of us had exchanged a word.

I cleaned off the smudge my nose left on the glass, picked up the bucket and walked out. I made sure to lock the door and empty the bucket. It was only when I locked the door and started back that I realised I had no idea to which one of us the new display belonged.

Trapping the Echo
by Lal Dhillon

'Remind me to plan our next night out myself,' Norman muttered surreptitiously to Lee, as the two friends made a clumsy game of integrating into the crowded hall.

Lee patted him on the back and flashed him a smile. 'Listen, I got us in, didn't I?' he responded. 'Don't worry, I know they looked a little fierce on the doors, but it's a museum, not a bloody palace. Relax and enjoy yourself, I've heard good things about this place.'

Norman sighed, brushed the man's hand off of his shoulder, and looked around. In fairness to his friend, the hall they had just entered was considerably more adorned than he would have expected it to be for the purposes of a museum fundraiser. Above him, oil lanterns hung among chandeliers, and here and there were sculptures designed to hold candles. Turning slowly above the centre of the room was a particularly elegant object made of blown glass: two serpents with black and white scales wound in embrace, each devouring the other's tail. The lights and flickering shadows combined with the brightly coloured figures dancing around the room in a disorienting movement that made Norman's head hurt. Eventually his eyes alighted upon the bar and, realising Lee had already gone off to talk to someone he knew, Norman forded his way through the sea of people towards it.

He pulled up a stool and perused the rack of expensive bottles with a sense of trepidation, weighing the financial sacrifice against the prospect of enduring the rest of the night sober, until, with some emotional strain, he reached for his wallet. However, before he could bankrupt himself he was interrupted.

'Careful. Don't reveal how much you've got to donate just yet,' a voice cautioned him.

Startled, he turned and found himself confronted by the most striking pair of eyes he had ever seen, pale green and smooth as beach glass. Words caught in his throat as the woman beside him went on. 'You don't need your wallet at an open bar. Try again.'

Norman nodded and placed a modest order. The woman next to him groaned, rubbing her eyes between forefinger and thumb. 'Scratch that,' she said, 'he'll have the same as me.'

She glanced sharply at him as the barman muttered a hurried 'yes ma'am' and turned away to pour another glass.

'No one orders the cheapest drink at an open bar. I gather this isn't exactly your scene, but you must have at least been to a wedding before. They still have open bars at weddings, right?'

Norman raised his eyebrows. 'I suppose it depends

on how good your friends are,' he replied, drawing an unexpected laugh from the woman as the barman put his drink on the counter.

'And how good are your friends, Mr...?' the woman asked with a wry smile.

'Call me Norman,' he answered, lifting his drink to his nose. 'And this probably isn't the night to ask me that.'

'Well then, it's rather lovely to meet you, Norman,' she replied. 'You can call me Heather. And I'm afraid you gave the wrong answer.'

'Trust me, if you'd met Lee, you'd know that was very much the right answer.'

The woman beside him laughed again. 'Oh, I don't really care about the other people you know. I meant that, now the two of us have met, your list of friends should be looking a lot healthier.'

Norman took a conspicuously long drink. 'All right, friend,' he said, looking down into his glass. 'What was it that gave me away?'

'You mean aside from the suit, the shoes, and the fact that you spent a good five minutes trying to identify the cheapest whisky at an open bar?'

Despite himself, Norman half smiled into his glass. 'Fair cop, I suppose. In fairness though, what sort of fundraiser is it that gives out free drinks?'

He looked up to find Heather's eyes glimmering at him. 'The sort which offers more exciting opportunities for investment. Speaking of which,' she said as she drew a little closer, glancing around the room, 'I was wondering whether you might be able to help a girl out. See, I'm looking to invest in their project, and I'm in need of a partner – someone who isn't well known around here. You would be compensated well.'

Norman frowned. 'Seems a little clandestine.'

'Well, of course,' she replied. 'Haven't you realised where we are?'

'A publicly owned cultural centre looking to keep the lights on?'

She shook her head and went on. 'The past is a powerful thing, Norman.' She ran her fingertip around the rim of her glass as she spoke, looking straight at him. 'It's the one thing we can't hold on to, yet institutions such as this are devoted to just that – the preservation of things that cannot be preserved, the pursuit of things long since lost. The world makes its music, and we do our best to trap the echoes. Believe me when I say that people will do the unthinkable to hold onto the past. And that's why I want to invest in the project. And it's why you should want to, too.'

As she spoke, a ringing cut through the air around them, and the hall gradually fell silent.

'It's time for the presentation then,' she said, turning to the centre of the room. 'Listen, and make your choice.'

Norman followed her eyeline, and saw an older man standing in the centre of the room, just below the turning serpents.

'Good evening, friends old and new,' he said. 'Don't worry, I won't keep you long from your drinks – after all, I'm the one who's paying for them.' There was a splashing of laughter around the room. 'For those of you I've yet to meet, allow me introduce myself: I am the curator of this museum. Now, I trust you're all feeling generous, and that you have come here ready to invest in our work. But before you commit, I want to give you just a small impression of what you may find yourself funding.'

He raised his hand and clicked his fingers, and a regiment of servers emerged behind him, each carrying a silver tray. 'Ladies and gentlemen, I invite you each to take one of the items which are being passed around the room. Inside, you should find something that looks rather like this.' He held up a thin strip of paper. As he spoke, a server approached Norman and offered him the tray. Cautiously, Norman reached out and took one of the objects, a thin and hollow shell that crumbled between his fingers, revealing the paper. 'Now,' the curator instructed, 'if you would be so kind, place two fingers together at the end of the parchment, and at your leisure pinch them tight.'

Norman complied with the first instruction and drew his breath in as the world around him was remade, the crowded room giving way to an open horizon. Above him, the ceiling peeled back to reveal a blue sky, and sand came up through the floor and enveloped his feet.

Looking around, he found himself flanked on either side by men in uniform who hung frozen mid-step. Behind him the ocean stretched on beyond the edge of the world, while the view inland was obscured by a curtain of sand caught in the air. The sun beat down on his back as he stood on the silent beach.

Having found his bearings and calmed himself slightly, he gave the strip a sharp pinch as he had been instructed. There was a burst of noise, and with a sudden alacrity the scene around him was taken up into life. Soldiers moved in time, calling out instructions to one another over staccato gunfire. The curtain of sand now fallen, Norman could just about see inland. He raised his hand to his brow and squinted to see dark shapes on the horizon, dotted here and there along the ridge. Then there was a flash of light and the air pressed in around him as though he were trapped beneath the ocean – and then he was back, propped up at the bar alongside Heather, whose eyes weighed on him knowingly. Around him, guests rubbed their eyes and held their brows, some looking suspiciously at their drinks.

'Thank you for your time, my good friends,' the curator intoned. 'As you know, historians are not traditionally in the business of making new things, but it has long been my intention to make the echoes of the past just a little more tangible, as you just experienced. Let me assure you that any donations towards such an end will be well remembered, and any investments will be well rewarded. Do come and talk to me or one of my representatives, and we can discuss the terms.'

With that, he stepped down, and the noise in the room very gradually returned.

Norman looked sideways at Heather, who sat staring into her drink, stirring it gently with her straw.

'Well then,' she said, not looking up, 'do I have your interest?'

A Stroke of Luck
by Tessa Fenley

Was he crying? She tried to sneak a peek at the man in the drenched navy jumper, standing in one of the smaller and therefore more intimate rooms of the museum. He seemed transfixed by a fairly straightforward sculpture of a small-size worn trainer, covered in dust, mounted on and partly covered by rubble, possibly from torn down buildings or ancient sites. It obviously moved him, although she could not see why. It had an ordinary feel to it, much like one of her boys' discarded shoes, she thought, her eyes smiling.

The sculptor had written a comment in German on the bottom of the display which she could not read, but perhaps the man could. She went closer to see.

'The game is over. Our feet are so tired from walking endlessly that we are prepared to follow whomever promises healing.'

Feeling like an intruder on the most private of emotions, she turned to leave the room, and passing close by the man she noticed that his tears were trickling onto the sculpture, like a tap drip-dripping soundlessly. She wondered whether she should urge him to take a step back in case he damaged the display. She stopped and, glued to the spot, fidgeting with her long moist hair, she weighed her options.

'Sir, are you all right?'

The man did not respond. Lightly touching his arm, she encouraged him to take a step back. Slowly, he lifted his head and they made eye contact. He looked foreign, definitely Arab.

'Are you all right?'

This time, the man nodded, accepting the tissue she offered him.

'My son,' he muttered. He was obviously in need of a friendly chat.

'Can I offer you a cup of tea?'

The man shrugged and she gently steered him in the direction of the museum's teashop. While he sat down somewhat awkwardly on the wooden bench, leaning against the green liberty-style wallpaper, she ordered a pot of tea and two slices of lemon drizzle cake. Taking the chair opposite him, she finally introduced herself.

'I'm Amy.' She extended her hand which he gently shook.

'I'm Muhad.'

His diffident smile made her take to him and she wondered if she should try and make small talk or let silence prevail. Perhaps he needed to get something off his chest.

Tea was served and while Amy poured, Muhad broke the silence, 'I only walked in here because it was raining and the notice said free entrance.' That made Amy chuckle.

The ice broken, she explained that she was a devoted friend of the museum and considered it her second home. His shy smile encouraged her to take the leap: 'I couldn't help but notice you seemed moved by one of the displays.'

Muhad tucked into his slice of lemon drizzle, the question left suspended in mid-air. After a while, he said, 'I'm originally from Syria, but I have fled my country. The destruction caused by the war, and the lack of safety wore my family down until we decided to make a run for it. My wife and I were determined to offer our children a future in a safe, politically stable country. One day, at dusk, we embarked on our journey to the border. My wife and daughter carried some of our belongings while I carried my son on my back to make as much progress as possible before nightfall.'

Amy put down her fork and nodded, stunned by his sudden openness. She tried to picture the scene: an anxious family travelling towards hope.

'We planned on travelling to Europe together, but it was too arduous for my pregnant wife. I left her and my daughter with an aunt in Aleppo while my son and I continued our journey. Feeling safer as we approached Turkey, we thought we were home free until a maverick band of rebels in a large SUV nearly ran us down and took a few shots at us. I leapt into the rubble, crawling for shelter, dragging my boy along with me. Just when I believed we were safe, I spotted blood seeping from his ears and nose. He had been hit and there was nothing I could do to save him. I had to remain hidden for the sake of my wife and daughter. I would be no use to them dead. So I sat there, watching my son struggle for breath and drawing blood instead of air. I remained by his side, held his hand, sheltered him with my own body to keep him warm, but to no avail. He died very quickly. Mercifully.'

Amy stared at him, unable to speak. What was there to say anyway? Instead, she reached out and put her hand over his.

Muhad wiped his tears and continued. 'At night, I intended to bury my son and move on as quickly as possible. When I checked the road for military vehicles, I noticed one of my son's shoes lying in the middle of the murky road, covered in dust. I retrieved it and put it back on his foot before I laid him to rest. They were his favourite trainers, you see.' Muhad sipped his tea and wiped his moustache with the paper napkin.

Amy took a deep breath. 'I cannot even begin to imagine the horror you went through before you got here. You must miss your son terribly.'

'I pray for him every day.'

'What about your wife and daughter? Have you been

reunited?' Amy asked with a tremor to her voice.

Muhad nodded. 'Yes, we share a small flat here, but life is expensive and I still have not found a job. My wife cleans for the neighbours and keeps us afloat.'

'What did you do back in Syria? Your English is impressive, if you don't mind my saying so.'

Muhad's eyes sparkled briefly at the unanticipated compliment. 'I worked on the oncology ward of the university hospital doing research and follow-up of patients after their treatment.'

Amy's mind was racing, wondering whether she knew someone who could help Muhad land a job. 'Tell you what, my dad is administrator at the local nursing home. It's not exactly a hospital, but perhaps he can point you in the right direction.'

Muhad flushed pink. 'But why?' he asked.

'Why what?'

'Why help me? You don't even know me.'

'We all need a stroke of luck from time to time and perhaps I can be yours.' Amy smiled as Muhad took her hand and squeezed it firmly.

'Thank you.' he whispered.

'You're welcome.'

He wrote down his phone number on a napkin and Amy promised to call him later that evening.

*

On his way home, Muhad dropped by the small improvised mosque and spent a long time praying.

Praying for redemption, for failing to save his son. Uttering words of gratitude for his precipitous encounter with Amy. And praying for Amy, that she too might one day meet her stroke of luck.

Extinct Monsters
by Mike Evis

'Cor! It's massive! Look at the size of this place!' yelled J right in my ear. Sometimes he really acts his age. Like, he's three months younger than me and you can tell. I call him J 'cause he's got this really, really, unusual name. No one in our entire class can say it, not even me. It's so long your tongue trips over it. I don't think he minds me calling him J though.

'Hey – check out these monsters over here!' he went on.

'That's why this hall's so big,' I said. 'They'd never fit them all in otherwise.'

'And just look at this one! Wow!'

Even I felt a bit, well, scared, standing in front of such a fierce looking creature, as though it might suddenly spring to life. It stood towering miles above our heads, many times the height of an adult, on its hind legs, paws raised as if at any second it could reach down and pluck us from the ground.

'Awesome!' said J as the rest of the class filed in.

'Ugh, it's so ugly,' said someone. Several girls giggled, but nervously rather than real laughter.

Our teacher stood to one side, right next to the guide, who leant casually against the monster's leg as if it were just a stone pillar, rather than a leg belonging to some creature so terrible it could reach down and eat you without even thinking about it.

'Don't worry, children,' said the museum guide, 'it's just a life-size model. The real life one died out some sixty-five million years ago. Yes?'

'Why did they die out?' asked someone near the front.

'Class, there will be plenty of time to ask questions at the end,' said our teacher, but the guide waved him aside.

'It's all right, it's a very good question. I was coming to that next,' said the guide.

'As I was saying, sixty-five million years ago,' he continued, peering over his glasses awkwardly – I held back a giggle – 'these ferocious creatures ruled the entire world. Nowhere was safe from them. Huge packs of them roamed all over the surface of the earth, stripping it bare of all life, eating anything they came across – animals, plants – anything edible.'

'So what happened to them?' asked someone else.

Our teacher looked annoyed but said nothing.

'We don't really know. There are many theories. Some experts suggest the population crashed because there were so many of them their numbers had grown to unsustainable levels. Some believe they caused their own extinction because they were such ferocious killers they drove other species to extinction, which left them with nothing to eat. But the most popular theory – and the one I like – is that a giant meteor hit the earth, causing millions and millions of tons of dust to rise into the air and black out the sun for a couple of years, killing all plant life and ninety-five percent of animal life. Within a few months they were all dead, leaving us to inherit the earth. We are the descendants of the five per cent.'

'So they're no longer around?'

'Class, I'm not going to tell you again. Don't interrupt.'

'No,' said the guide, smiling. 'You don't have to worry about bumping into one. They're all long dead. The only place you'll find them is in a museum like this. But while they roamed the earth they were the most deadly, the most violent, the most destructive species the earth has ever known.'

'Awesome,' said J. 'I absolutely have to get a model from the museum shop.'

'Me too!' I said.

'You've got two already.'

'Yeah, but with three I can stage battles between them.'

'So,' continued the guide, 'imagine a warm day, some sixty-five million years ago. Our gaze scans over a large herd of these creatures, hurrying, bustling about and knocking against each other – sounds scary, doesn't it, children? You wouldn't want to be there, would you?'

'No,' some muttered.

'This whole area would have been low-lying marshland, sloping down to the sea. Judging by the remains we've found, they would come here to bask in the sun and relax.'

'Cor,' said J, pointing to another of the monsters, housed in a gigantic glass case. 'It says here this one comes to life. You just have to press this button here.'

'You going to?' I said.

'Shall I?' We laughed.

The life-size model, like the one next to it, stood many times higher than us. It reached all the way to the museum roof. As the guide droned on, we giggled as the monster slowly came to life, as if it had been asleep, just waiting for us to wake it. Its ugly face became even more horrible as its mouth curled into a snarl. It made a terrible grimace, then lurched forward, and I couldn't help flinching. It was so realistic, if it hadn't been for the glass case I'd have wanted to run straight out of there. But don't tell J I said that. Baring its teeth, its eyes glared hatred at us and it flexed its limbs, as if ready to grasp us. It stomped towards the edge of the glass, all the while making fearsome noises.

'Wow, imagine if they had a full-size version of that in the shop.'

J shrugged. 'They might have a toy version – bound to, it's got to be the fiercest one they've got.'

One of the girls in the class screamed loudly, and the

teacher looked round.

'Who turned this on?' he said, glaring at us all.

'Never mind,' said the guide, moving to the front of the model as it continued to threaten and make ferocious sounds. 'This illustrates just how fierce a predator this creature would have been. Look at the teeth. Our ancestors – had they been around in those days – wouldn't have stood a chance.'

'This is the best thing in the museum,' I said.

'Yeah, the rest of it is totally dull.'

'All those vases and stuff.'

'Boring.'

The guide was still talking.

'And over here is one of the most perfectly preserved specimens. This one is not a model, it's the actual body, perfectly preserved in ice near the Pole.'

'It's repulsive,' said someone.

'Were they really that funny colour?'

The guide continued. 'Imagine the terror other animals must have felt when they realised they were being stalked by this creature. None would stand a chance against it. This species knew no fear at all.'

'Sometimes,' the guide went on, 'they would fight among themselves – we're not really sure why – it could be they were battling for food, for territory, supremacy, or for some other reason we don't understand. As you might imagine, such contests were very violent indeed, and usually deadly. Now, any questions?'

'Why don't they have fur, and scales, like us?' said a girl. 'They just look… horrible.'

'They are repulsive, aren't they? Although I've worked in this area for some years, I still find it hard to warm to them. All that naked, pale skin, the absence of a tail – they really do look rather strange. We can only be glad they're completely extinct.' He swished his tail, pushing his glasses up. 'Does anyone have any further questions, before we leave the human section of the extinct species department?'

History has a Way of Repeating Itself
by Jody Kish

'Come in, come in. Welcome to the Museum of a World Forgotten. The first exhibit is to your left. Let me open the door for you.'

Eyeing the man with curiosity, Ethan walked into the large room.

'Please find a seat, this by far is our most popular exhibit. The large amphitheatre allows for perfect viewing of this magnificent forty-one foot Earth, which rotates on a motorised axis. A perfect technological rendition created using satellite imagery compiled into a complex database incorporating bathymetry and terrain cartography. Oceans, clouds, the continents, and even subtle changes to Earth's atmosphere are identified using state-of-the-art sensors.'

Ethan was in awe of the enormous sphere.

'And all of this was created by yours truly.'

Blue eyes peered directly at Ethan. 'How ironic that this very technology is causing Earth's inevitable demise.' The man furrowed his brow and adjusted his glasses.

Cocking his head, Ethan scrutinised the stranger, noticing the man's nametag. Dim light reflected on a golden badge with large black letters, E-T-H-A-N.

'It's quite impressive,' the man went on. 'Our museum is the first of its kind. Would you like to see what happens if Earth continues on the course it's heading along?'

Shaking his head, but knowing the man would ignore his reluctance, Ethan waited. His foot tapped the wooden floor in anticipation; his excitement boiling in the pit of his stomach.

'Now, as we look at the globe, you'll observe Earth as it changes, very subtly at first. Here, let me show you what happens.' He typed frantically on a glass keyboard.

So much of what the man said were thoughts that Ethan ruminated on in a recurring dream, but how–?

'Once-blue skies will turn a sludge brown, and Earth will become a desert, while it awaits its end.'

Ethan looked around, expecting to see others reacting to the doom and gloom, but he saw only obscured faceless shapes around him.

What was going on?

'It's up to us to set it right. A museum can only show us our past and present. But we can use the knowledge gained to create a better future – we can avoid making the mistakes we've identified here.' The man sighed. 'Technology has been absorbed into every part of our lives. Think about it: smartphones, the internet – and even books. Digital this, digital that. When was the last time you held a book, smelled the pages as you turned them, felt the texture of paper between your fingers, and proudly put it on a shelf knowing it would patiently wait for you to read it again? We've become accustomed to having everything instantly, and discarding it after use. It makes our lives easier, yes, but what has our appetite cost us?'

'Ethan! Ethan! Wake up!' Josh shook his brother, startling him awake. Toppling from his chair, a dazed Ethan found himself at the library surrounded by stacks of science books. Scattered notes were spread out on the table before him.

Ethan looked up at his brother: Josh could never understand why Ethan was so enamored of science and time travel. He complained when Ethan went on about wormholes and bridges to other worlds.

'Daydreaming again?' he said now. 'Come on, Ethan, let's get back home. Mum and Dad are gonna be mad if we're late again.'

*

Years had passed since Earth had started over – or 'The Change' as Ethan named it.

Josh nudged his brother and pointed at an old man across the road from where they stood. The man's thin gnarled fingers held tight to a makeshift walking stick; leathered skin and sunken blue eyes stared back across the street.

Ethan grunted in response. 'Yeah, he's an old man.

Haven't seen one of them in years.'

His brother continued to gawk at the leathered man.

Skeletons of buildings cast ghostly silhouettes while light from the sun struggled to break through the grey clouds. A sulphur smell hung in once oxygen-rich air; they breathed shallowly, masks tied to their faces.

'Come on, Ethan. Let's find somewhere to sleep.' Josh kicked at soil around his feet and a swirl of dust engulfed them, then dispersed in the biting breeze, which tore at their exposed skin. Simultaneously, they shuddered. It was time to head toward shelter. Ethan turned to his younger brother nodding in unspoken agreement.

Across the road, the old man's leathered face cracked into a grin. Then he disappeared between piles of rubble.

The basement of a toppled church offered the brothers temporary protection, allowing them brief solace from the harsh elements outside. Emaciated bodies riddled the floor, five of them. Together they had survived what had made the sky brown and landscape a dreary, desolate wasteland. Each passing day, however, was becoming more laborious. How had the old man survived this long – and alone?

A symphony of snores echoed in the darkness. Ethan lay awake. Noticing that the wind had died down, he snuck out into the night, draping his torn blanket over his shoulders. He made his way into the heart of the city, guided by the dim glow of the moon and stars, which were themselves obscured from view by the dust in the air.

Ethan found his way back to the crumbling buildings where he had seen the leather-faced man. Between two piles of rubble was a massive structure with broken pillars. The letters M-U-S-E clung to the front.

A voice whispered behind him, 'You're back.'

Ethan span around and felt a rush of panic. 'Uh, hi. Uh, yeah. I'm sorry. I just–'

'No need to be afraid. Sit. Please. I don't get a lot of company these days.' A toothless grin exposed the black pit of his mouth.

Cast in shadows from a single candle, Ethan sat in dirt alongside the hunched-over man.

'This was a museum. You may remember it from the days before the Earth swallowed everything up.' The man shook his head. 'How awful it is to bear witness to such a tragedy. People, the sky, the world as we knew it. Our lives changed, just like that!' He snapped his gnarled fingers, causing Ethan to cringe – his fingers looked so brittle he feared they might break and the pieces tumble to the ground like the buildings that surrounded them.

'Have I seen you before?' Ethan squinted at the old man. 'Were you–'

The old man looked at Ethan with sadness. His shoulders sagged. 'Yes, yes. This is all my fault. Our invention. If I had only… but you've forgotten my warning. I tried to tell you. It's up to you now.'

Ethan looked at the man. 'You… you are… but how?'

'It's not too late. Stop The Change.'

The man evaporated into particles that mixed with the air, and Ethan could only stare in shocked realisation.

*

Memories resurfaced, slamming into Ethan's subconscious.

He awoke in his bedroom.

Breathing heavily, fearful of finding himself in an apocalyptic world, Ethan was coated in sweat. But he was home. He turned to see his younger brother fast asleep, cocooned in the safety of his comforter in bed opposite him. Not the church. No apocalypse.

Ethan thought about his dream, about the dreams that had recurred for years. He thought about the technology, and about the old man that was himself in another life.

Ethan T Holt, was a genius and inventor of the biggest technological breakthrough when he was a teenager. Solving the mystery of the Einstein-Rosen bridges, space-time, or time travel as some would call it, he'd discovered how to leap into one of many wormholes correcting previous damage to the planet. But in doing so, he altered the axis of Earth, and thus created an apocalyptic event – The Change.

Each time he went back in time to rectify his error and warn his younger self, the results were the same: disastrous!

He realised the ultimate sacrifice he would have to make, but would it work? Could it work?

He examined the book of scribbled notes on his desk, full of his research and where he had first recorded his monumental discovery. He smelled its pages, felt the texture between fingers and...

Vanished.

*

The museum stood out from smaller buildings packed to each side. Its brick walls housed many fascinating discoveries, which served as reminders to younger generations. Bronze statues of some of the greatest inventors welcomed visitors upon entering between the marble pillars and through its massive mahogany doors.

Josh's heart swelled with pride as little fingers squeezed his hand. 'And this is your uncle's name on the placard. Ethan T Holt.' With his other hand, Josh ran his fingertips over the raised letters. 'They dedicated a wing of the museum to his unfinished research.'

The little boy listened intently.

'He just disappeared.' Josh raised his hands in an exaggerated gesture.

That night, Josh tucked his son into the plush

bedding, and gave him a kiss on the forehead.

'What story would you like Daddy to tell you tonight? How about a story about wormholes? Yes, wormholes. Did you know that they could take you wherever you want to go? Your uncle told me all about them. He even showed me.'

A tired voice replied.

'What? You'd likc to visit your uncle?'

What harm could come from a simple visit?

Lost Goddesses
by Charles Bonkowsky

Stained glass glimmers in the harsh lights of the museum, the colours faded from so many years of throwing sunlight on worshippers. The glass is framed in gold, as though that could make up for the fact it has been stolen – as though the paper label could equal the years of history every priest and attendant knows by heart.

Naliaka, their goddess, is built of angles and straight lines.

'Why did you leave us?' Eshe whispers, standing small and alone among the seemingly endless rows of display cases. 'Why did you let them bring you here? They won't let us pray to you anymore…'

Her voice falls, fading despite the hard tiles surrounding her. She shouldn't be here, but this is the only place she can find Naliaka, picking through the fragments of what used to be her temple. This is the only place they saved her, locked away in the soulless vaults of this museum, far from the eyes of her faithful.

'You won't answer anymore. Is it because we failed you?' It is the only explanation Eshe can think of. Others, the survivors hollow-eyed from grief, have told her every detail of that failure: how it is their fault the goddess left. Because of their misdeeds, the sand was stained with blood and the sky had burnt with fire. They had brought the strange and terrible men from over the sea, the men who dissected their halls, dismantled the stone walls that generations had built.

Light lines her face, the strip-bulbs gleaming on the tears that track down her face. 'Can't you tell me why?'

Oh, child. The voice comes from nowhere and everywhere, feels more than heard in the breeze that caresses her face. *You have travelled so far to get here, and for what?*

'For – for you,' she says. 'Everything is... falling apart without you, without your help. They try to pretend it's not,' she says, glancing behind her as if they'll hear, as if they'll appear to insist once more that everything is fine, 'but...I don't even know how much longer we'll last. Please.'

They had tried. They had built shrines of rubble and brick in the shadow of fallen temples, only for them to be kicked down. They had muttered hurried prayers, which were shouted over and rewarded with nothing but silence from above.

I'm sorry, the goddess says at last.

'Sorry? Why? We failed you. We let them take you, let them stop us–'

No. The word echoes in the space not designed for it, rattling dry containers and knocking labels off their objects. *You did not fail me.*

Eshe blinks, frowns, opens her mouth but can't form

the words. 'I don't understand. They ripped every image from the walls, they tore down your statues and melted them, and we – we hid instead of fighting them, instead of fighting for you–'

I failed you. The voice that gave the Proclamations, tinged with sadness. *You fought when I did not, could not. You claim yourselves not worthy of my patronage – I know myself not worthy of your following. Forgive me,* she whispers, the voice of the moon and sun and stars. *Please.*

'I–' Eshe swallows the words. 'I… if you truly think so, why not help us now? Come back.'

Glass ripples and softens, condensation forming impossibly in the dry room. *I cannot. I am not a goddess of war, nor even of the hunt. I cannot save you, child. But perhaps…*

She can't see her through the glass, barely knows that her Naliaka is behind it. 'Perhaps?' she demands, letting her frustration, her anger, boil over. 'You are supposed to be our goddess! You're supposed to help us, why won't you now?'

You. You made it here, deep into the heart of your enemy. There is a fire in you, Eshe, a fire I could never possess. I was the goddess of the harvest, of creation and growth, but this is not the time. Now is the time of blades, now is the time of the flames that I can see burning at your core.

'What do you mean? Why won't you just tell me–?' Somehow, sunlight gleams behind the panels, a beam of light glancing off the corners of the window and into her eyes.

I am telling you. This is not my time. The light shatters, a million lines wrapping themselves around her. She gasps, eyes blazing in the stream of colours from the stained glass. The colours of the goddess.

It's yours.

Underground
by Adele Evershed

Every year I get one month off to spend on Earth. My home is in the Capital Colony, Sanfrany Bunker. Each time I visit Earth I'm amazed by all the new innovations. Not just medical breakthroughs in robo-parts or synthetic meat-eats but things like projections of your face as you pass by showing you enjoying things like the anti-grav spa – today I saw myself drinking the new trendy AspaNectar in the Watering Hole Bar; I was having a great time!

There is a park where the fountains bloom with virtual water; they look real enough that young children jump into them expecting to make a splash. Of course, they are disappointed. Yesterday I heard a toddler cry when he discovered the water was like a dream that disappeared when he woke. It's not a sound you often hear, even when children fall over and scrape a knee. His mother scooped him up, licking his precious tears, telling him, 'Hush now, don't waste your water,' and then she persuaded him to play on the turbo swing.

I could be spoilt for choice deciding what to spend my work chips on, but I always head to the Community History Museum. My mum used to take me there, before she floated. In this ever-changing underground world it is the one place that stays the same.

As you pass through the ancient doors, made from real wood, you see a quote carved into the stone lintel. It's from Prophet Stephen King, *Each life makes its own imitation of immortality.* Nan says they're the only words on Earth that are literally carved in stone. Nan doesn't like the museum much. She says, 'It wounds with wonders that we'll never know.' When she speaks like that, Dad rolls his eyes. He used to tell her to be careful as it might sound like she is criticising the Community but now she's so close to her floating he lets her be.

Nan will visit the Hall of Signs though. It was Mum's favorite place because that's where she met my dad. He was at the museum on his day off from the RoboLab and she volunteered there as a tour guide. Dad was laughing uproariously, so much so everybody in the hall was looking at him wondering what was so funny in this hallowed place of learning. Mum walked over and saw he was shaking his head and pointing at a faded chipped sign labeled 'San Francisco 1908'. It said 'No Pissing In The Alley'.

Dad looked at Mum and said, 'Can you believe it? There was a time when people had to be told not to make water in an alley! They could literally piss it away rather than upcycle.'

'Not the best chat-up line,' Mum always said, but they spent the rest of the day together and, 'The rest is history,' Dad would add.

When I visit the museum with Nan I leave her in the Hall of Signs. She also likes to spend time wandering around the virtual graveyard. They project different stones, she claims, so you never see the same inscriptions twice. When I asked her why she spends so much time there she said, 'I'm composing what I'd want on my gravestone if I could be buried and not floated.'

When I told Dad, he said, 'Your Nan should be more Community-minded and be glad her hair, teeth and bones will be upcycled. They're her legacy, never mind that her name is not recorded anywhere. And why would anyone want to be buried anymore?'

He's right. We live underground all our lives, at least when we're floated our essence gets released into the Toxy.

Then he said, 'And at least she gets to keep her True Day.' He carried on almost to himself, 'Not like your poor Mum.'

Mum was diagnosed with lung cancer at one of her six-month checks. It is one of our biggest killers. The air vents do the best they can to filter the radioactive particles from the Toxy but still some get through. The Community doesn't have the resources to cope with serious diseases, so if you don't get the all clear from the doctors then you have to be floated. You have a 'water week', where you can blub as much as you like, and after that you join the other floaters – the old, who have reached their 'True Day', and the sick, the ones that are 'floated too young' like my mum.

When Mum was floated, I was away working on Lunar Station North and didn't find out until I got leave eight months later. I was expecting Nan or Dad to tell me, 'It's too late to blub now. Don't waste your water,' but neither of them did. Nan even pressed a blub catcher in my hand before I closed my hatch on my first night home.

I like the Hall of Nature best. When I was a kid you could touch real grass or put your hand in a tank to pet a live Longtail Shrimp. Those exhibits have gone now but they do have a robo-shrimp, which feels almost like the real thing. It was one of the oldest animal species on the planet but obviously there are no freshwater creatures anymore.

Now the only real animals you can see are horseshoe crabs. The sooty armour that ensured their survival makes them look like a pet for an alien boy. The info panel says they have blue blood and our scientists use them for testing vaccines.

When I told Nan, she snorted and said, 'They need to rechristen themselves, the horseshoe moniker hasn't been that lucky for them has it?'

I asked her what she meant; they were one of the few animals that survived the Toxy.

She said, 'Oh, love, don't mind me, but sometimes I

think we weren't meant to survive.'

Nan has always questioned our history. She got into trouble at her graduation for reading a poem she had written. According to Dad it was a slice of truth that the Community didn't want served. She had been assigned to 'Communications' but after that she was put on 'Sieve' detail. She spends her life sieving dirt for items to be upcycled.

Today we found out that the aqua ration is going to be cut again. When Nan heard she grumbled, 'It's not just those crabs that need a new name. They should start calling the Community the Con-munity, they're just a bunch of con artists. How come they keep telling us that the mines are doing great, maximum production blah, blah and in the next breath cut our daily aqua?'

People think with my job we get extra rations but we don't. Everybody knows mining water on the moon is tough, and nobody wants to get selected for this detail. I remember when my name was called, on my sixteenth birthday. Even Dad sucked in his cheeks. I'm a Diviner; it's my job to find the juiciest chunks of water-ice. Lately, it's become harder and harder to locate good bricks. Most of the time I'm finding slush mixed with moon dust, which is much more difficult to extract.

Just before I left the moon I heard a rumour that the station at South Lunar Pole was exhausted. I haven't told Nan and Dad. What would be the point? Nan is always saying, 'I'm on the edge of a good blubbing', and I don't want to be the one that pushes her over. Dad would tell me that I should stop wasting my leave exploding water bombs on my family and go and spend my work chips at the Watering Hole. Anyway, I know the Community has all our argonauts scouring space for new mining opportunities so I have faith it will all be fine.

As you leave the museum there is another quote from Prophet King. It's projected on the wall so it wobbles like a mirage: 'Fiction is the truth inside the lie'. It reminds me of Nan's poem from her graduation. She wants me to read it at her floating but I'm not sure that's a good idea.

Skull Bank
by Charles Osborne

We are the Apapraxos. We live near the sea. We are a peaceful people. Each morning, a dozen or so of us make our way to the coast to fish. We set out in our small canvas-covered sailing boat. Patrolling pink-nosed dolphins, green-necked turtles, and blue-grey flying fish see us on our way.

The outgoing tide skips and ripples along the side of the small boat. We look to the horizon. The weather is changing. We press on.

Clouds skim, bulbous balloons of black unfold. As the darkness builds, the atmosphere changes mysteriously. The waves whip up into fast running swells. The boat rocks from side to side. A larger wave than the rest suddenly takes the boat up on its crest and drags it deep down again; the boat is swamped. We manage to make it to a nearby sandbank half hidden in swaying blue-green reed grass. Rocks, unseen, tear a hole in the boat. We lay on the hot sand, exhausted.

Some weeks later, when the bad weather subsides, a small band of women and the village shaman set out in search of us. They search the bay. As evening descends, they come upon the sandbank. All they find are white skeletal remains bleached by the sun, the flesh eaten away by local crabs, lizards, and marauding sea birds.

With much effort, a shallow mass grave is dug. Our spears, tridents, and precious rings and bracelets, are buried with us. We are placed east, to face the rising sun. A mound of rocks is laid over us. The shaman offers us up to the other life. The women depart in tears, full of sorrow.

Every year, at the summer solstice, a group of surviving villagers sails over to the half-hidden sandbank to pay homage to the dead and to make offerings to the gods. One year sickness racked the village. The village elders decided not to make the hazardous journey. The gods were angry.

Later that same year, invaders swept in from the sea and burnt the village. Those of the villagers who escaped the looting and plunder headed for the nearby mountain pass and up into the hills. They were now dispersed, and few in number.

They were never to visit us again.

Over the ensuing years ferocious storms persisted. The sandbank shifted and eventually disappeared.

*

A racing catamaran, off-course and badly damaged, heaves to on an uncharted sandbank. A crewman spots a protruding skull. After temporary repairs, the catamaran makes for the nearest harbour. The police are informed. An investigation begins. Archaeologists are called in when initial tests suggest the skulls are historical. A wider audience is needed. A deal is struck. Our skulls are loaded onto an afternoon flight for London.

On arrival in London, archaeologists take the skulls for further laboratory tests. To the surprise of the archaeologists, the skulls are found to date from around 3ooo BC. 'Who are these people? Where do they come from?' they ask.

After thousands of years, only our bleached skulls remain; a marker of our existence. After detailed investigation and examination our skulls are carefully placed in glass display cabinets; we are specimens on show. People come to gawp and stare, ignoring ancient rites and beliefs, respect forgotten.

We miss our ancient resting place, the call of the seabirds, the sound of the wind and the sea.

*

The judge is summing up.

'While I have some sympathy for the three defendants, who claim to be descendants of the Apapraxos, we are not here to judge this issue on moral grounds. What the jury needs to address is whether, by their actions of breaking into the museum and stealing these ancient remains, that is, the Apapraxos skulls, the defendants have knowingly broken the law and committed an offence. It is no defence for the accused to plead that there is no case to answer.

'Although the accused argue that the skulls have been stolen and rightly belong to them, as Apapraxo descendants, the law, as it stands, does not give them the automatic right to retrieve that which has not been determined as legally theirs. This is a matter which is subject to negotiation between the museum and the indigenous people. Whatever the merits, or otherwise, of their actions, the defendants had no right to take the law into their own hands.'

The skulls were never found. Each of the defendants was found guilty and sentenced to a term in prison.

'Skulduggery at local museum,' the headline read. 'Theft of skulls after museum refuses to release the so-called Apapraxos skulls. A spokesperson for the museum said that this decision had been made on purely scientific grounds. CCTV evidence produced in court showed that an employee had been in cahoots with two so-called Apapraxoans in the theft. Despite extensive searches by the authorities the skulls have not been recovered.'

*

We had been away too long. The gods were not happy. They had watched over us for thousands of years. What remained of our people had been spread around the world. The gods had been like shepherds: shepherds of the dead, watching over our remains, keeping us safe and secure in the land we loved – in the land which formed part of our soul, our spirit: near to the sea-sprayed shoreline and surrounded by the sound of the seabirds, the shifting sandbanks, and the blue-green reed grass.

The little boat edged up the sandbank. Our skulls were carefully eased out of several sea-soaked sisal bags. A wizened old man, skilled in shamanic rites, had been found to lay us to rest. A small crowd gathered around the newly dug sand hole. The shaman's incantations flew in the wind. Seabirds circled.

That winter, a storm raged. The sandbank shifted, and disappeared.

Here, we lie, buried beneath the ocean, safe for another thousand years.

The School Trip
by Marsha Webb

'Come on now, make sure you hold your partner's hand. Jason stop picking your nose, that's not nice is it?' Mrs James was beginning to regret taking class 4C to the museum on a school trip. 'Rachel you've dropped your lunchbox, pick it up now, petal.'

Mrs James looked around for their guide while keeping one eye on the twenty-eight children. She and Miss Lean, her teacher's assistant, had brought them to the Science and Technology department.

'Miss Lean, can you stop Michael poking Gary, please, and take those leaflets off Gemma.' Gemma was pretending to be a teacher and giving the leaflets out to all her classmates with the instruction, 'Put this in your bag, it's your homework for later.' Miss Lean removed the leaflets and put them back on the shelf, then returned to resting her arm on the counter with a vacant stare into space.

Mrs James shook her head. Jane Lean was a nice girl, but what she would describe as a drip: she needed to be told step by step everything that needed doing, she had no initiative whatsoever. Sometimes it was like having an extra child in the classroom.

Her thoughts were interrupted by a young man in his twenties with pale skin and glasses, holding a sheet of paper. 'Is this Greenback Primary school?'

Before Mrs James had a chance to answer, Derek shouted out, 'Is that your boyfriend, Miss?'

After shooting him a warning look, Mrs James turned to the young man. 'Greenbrook, yes, hello, I'm Mrs James.' She scrutinised the skinny young chap over the top of her glasses. 'Oh dear,' she thought, 'they will eat him for breakfast.'

After a person has been teaching for a number of years they develop a sixth sense and are able to tell just by looking at someone whether or not they would be able to command the respect of the children – or, in layman's terms, whether the children will play them up or not.

'Right, children, listen carefully to the gentleman, he needs to talk to you.'

'Oh right, um, hi everyone, my name is, um, Peter,' he began.

'Umpeter, that's a funny name,' Ryan (at the front) commented. Kate (next to him) burst into fits of giggles.

'Don't be silly,' Mrs James scolded. 'His name is Peter, you know that.'

Ryan dropped his head slightly.

'Right,' Peter continued, already looking like he wanted to give up. 'So, I've got some, um, sheets that you need to fill in.'

Mrs James stared straight at Ryan, catching his eye,

pre-empting him asking what an umsheet was.

'So, we are going to look at the exhibits in the room and, um, then, um, fill in the sheets. OK?'

The children had already started fidgeting and talking. So much for having a day where she could step back: Mrs James knew she had to take over.

'Right, class, look this way. Miss Lean, hand out the sheets and the pencils, please.' Mrs James took the sheets from a relieved Peter.

After a barrage of pointless questions from the class, Peter led them into a vast dark room, the darkness interrupted by the exhibits, which were colourful and bright. The children were soon busy grabbing and pulling the interactive exhibits, and Mrs James was happy to finally have a minute to herself. This was soon spoiled by the familiar tug on her long pleated skirt.

'Miss, I need the toilet.' Kate Deacon's wide eyes were looking up at her, and she was shuffling from foot to foot in the telltale manner of a small child needing the bathroom. Normally Mrs James would have directed the child towards Miss Lean, but this time she spotted an opportunity. On arrival, Mrs James had noticed a lovely coffee shop near the foyer selling homemade biscuits, cakes and fresh filter coffee, and there were toilets directly opposite.

'Come on then, Kate. Miss Lean, I'm just popping Kate to the toilet.'

Miss Lean absentmindedly nodded.

'I need the toilet as well, Miss.'

Mrs James raised her eyebrows – why was it that you couldn't mention the word toilet in front of children without them all wanting to go? 'Come on then, quickly.' Mrs James ushered both the girls out before any more children wanted to join them.

Reaching the foyer, Mrs James knew that she had at least ten minutes to get her coffee and biscuit. Primary school children, especially girls, took an eternity in the toilets, mostly by the sink and the mirrors.

Lunchtime soon came and the pupils were led into the great hall, a beautiful, ornate high-ceilinged room with loads of space for the children to eat what remaining lunch they had not eaten on the bus on the way there. (The minute they had got on the bus, before even pulling out of the school carpark they began ripping open their lunchboxes and eating and drinking like they hadn't been fed in months.)

All was going well until Alan asked, 'Mrs James, where is Timmy?'

Mrs James scanned the room quickly and expertly. Timmy was definitely not there.

'Miss Lean, where is Timmy?'

Miss Lean shrugged. 'I haven't seen him since starting the activity.'

'Alan,' Mrs James tried to remain calm, 'when was the last time you saw Timmy?'

'When we were filling out our sheet,' Alan answered.

'Where did he go then?'

'I don't know,' shrugged Alan.

'Right, Miss Lean, you are going to have to supervise in here with Peter, I'm going to look for Timmy.' Mrs James tried to keep the panic out of her voice.

She ran to the security desk, they started systematically checking all the display rooms, calling out his name. The toilets were checked, the café and all the rooms near their exhibit room, but there was no sign of him. The chief of security went to check the CCTV and Mrs James felt like she might be heading for a full-scale meltdown. What if someone had taken him? She gave an involuntary shudder.

One of the young curators put a comforting hand on her shoulder. 'Don't panic yet, think like a child. What does he like?'

'Dinosaurs,' Mrs James replied without hesitation. 'Timmy loves dinosaurs.'

'Right. Upstairs. Follow me.' The curator hastily walked off, and Mrs James followed as fast as her exhausted body would carry her.

They burst through the door to the dinosaur exhibit, and found Timmy sitting on the floor.

'I've been in the dinosaur's tummy,' said Timmy proudly.

'Timmy!' yelled Mrs James. 'We have been worried sick about you, what did I say about wandering off on your own?'

Timmy put on his confused face. 'I don't know, Miss.'

Timmy was greeted by claps and cheers from the other pupils.

'Miss Lean told us they were getting the police to try and find you,' piped up Simon. That was something else she would have to speak to Miss Lean about. You always play down a situation where young children are concerned, so as not to add to the drama.

'No one was calling the police, Timmy was just looking at the dinosaurs.' Mrs James said.

'I want to see the dinosaurs,' came the chorus from the children.

'Sorry it's time to go now, the coach is waiting. Everyone grab your things, don't leave anything behind.'

Arriving at the school gates, Mrs James announced, 'Remember to tell your parents what a lovely time you had and how much you learned at the museum.'

After politely chatting to parents who took the opportunity of seeing her in the car park to ask about their child's progress (like some impromptu parents' evening), Mrs James walked towards her classroom. She had not had time for lunch and was hoping for a quick sandwich before preparing for tomorrow's lessons.

Hearing the banging and drilling coming from her

classroom Mrs James remembered they were having work done, and they obviously had not finished. It would be better to work at home. So she just picked up some resources and dragged her hungry body towards the door.

'Oh, I wish I was a teacher,' one of the workmen shouted. 'On a trip all day and a four o' clock finish. What a life.'

Mrs James forced a smile onto her face, gave a polite wave, and commended herself silently for resisting the temptation to punch him in the face.

Welcome to my Underworld
by John Ludlam

'Don't stare at one face, scan them all, it's easier to bring them up sharp.' Mr Senshall repeated his sergeant's advice into his shaving mirror, then pulled the curtain back just enough to look across at the pilgrim church opposite, with its king-size olive-green yew tree glistening in the morning sun. A fine early summer's day: warm already, it could get hotter than Italy. With at least one coach party from the Continent due today, there could be the most visitors this season.

After marrying and living on this rugged coast for thirty-seven years – and one more as a widower, Mr Senshall could commit himself completely to his vocation but for Ros, his daughter, trying to get him to spend time with her and her two children in her dreadful flat.

To Mr Senshall, his curatorship of the ossuary in the church crypt associated him with all the souls that had passed through on pilgrimage to pay homage to the saint, and those who had entered their eternal rest in this parish. Their bones were found buried beneath the south transept; once excavated and dated they were rehoused in a purpose-built crypt almost buried in the hill-side just below the church, and left in the care of Mr Senshall.

In a first floor flat across town, Ros, up first, swept a brush and comb through her hair, did her face, then called, 'Time for up! Up, up, up! If I have to come and get you....'

As the sun flooded his small bedroom with warm yellow, Thomas said, 'I don't love you,' to Henry his teddy bear, then watched in awe as breakfast and clothes issued out of the dark whirlwind that was his mother.

Organising childcare and fooling everybody at the office that she was on top of everything was a daily struggle for Ros. Nobody had explained about bringing up children, and the people she thought would help had vanished one by one. First Paolo, her partner, claiming he didn't fit in, took flight to look after his mother in Apulia; then her own mother died. She could recall her last sensible words, 'Get some help for Thomas, he needs a father. Try your dad, but you can't look after him as well – it's too late, he spends more time now with his ghosts.' A paucity of available men left Ros to spark a relationship with a local carpenter, twelve years older than herself.

*

Recruited at eighteen into his father's regiment, straight out of officer training, Senshall caught the end of the war in Europe, and experienced the sights and smells of mutilated bodies, severed limbs, and rotting carcasses. He did not bring back Leica binoculars, a bayonet or knife set, although some said he did have a souvenir, they had seen it.

The last miles of the advance through Italy were the most bitter; any of the enemy who did not surrender were hunted down. Elite German troops covered the retreat, exhibiting all the Spartan virtues of their military training. Such were the enemy who Senshall saw for the first time on the road to Ferrara, at a collection of houses enclosed by farmlands, where one disused building was now held by only two men.

Senshall led his platoon in to flush them out and take their surrender. The first man tried to run, and was shot. Throwing a stick grenade as a distraction, another soldier ran straight into the sergeant, Senshall's mentor on the battlefield. A blade flashed, and the sergeant fell.

Stunned, Senshall stood paralysed. Someone fired, wounding the German, and a veteran of the campaign wrested the knife from him.

By this stage of the war, no tally was kept of atrocities: each side, well aware of the other's fractured reputation, gave and expected only battlefield justice. Compelled to witness its course, Senshall was initiated into the honour code of silence. The trophy was dropped into a burlap sack and, with blood seeping through, it was passed to him.

*

The yew tree, by casting dense shade over the crypt, protects the bones against extremes of temperature throughout the year and, in gratitude, the bones keep the church and town in a little tourist business for, although the skeletons could not be reconstructed, at least their skulls could be displayed on shelves that ran the length of the crypt's inner wall. Strange companions, but without these friends Mr Senshall would be alone – except for his daughter and her brood.

Each time he visited Ros' flat he fell foul of a new obstacle course constructed from washing baskets, airers, discarded clothes and toys. Objects and surfaces brandished primary yellows, reds and blues as if torn from revolutionary tricolours marking out hostile territories.

Last Tuesday he got a blast of, 'At least you would think my father would help with his grandchildren. But no, you are even more into your crypt thing. Is it too much to ask for just one of the males in my life to be normal? Even Thomas is weird at four, and now his teddy bear, which I have to call Henry, counts as another one. I've certainly got the full set of male types to deal with!'

'Well, if you had done the sensible thing and married someone before having their children then perhaps the father–' he paused for a silent *whoever he was* '–would have accepted his responsibilities and you wouldn't keep needing my help.'

Just as Ros called him an old fossil, a pack of screaming children burst out from behind a door and raced around him like the Gadarene swine, scattering order and peace to the four winds. What a relief it was to leave; being there didn't make any sense.

As curator, Mr Senshall, instead of reading a bedtime story to Thomas and Henry, would rather take his stand in the crypt and rehearse one of his talks, addressing the ranks of skulls. He enjoyed the recasting of the bones as audience, particularly when, in an occasional zephyr of a draught, he detected soft murmurs of assent to his talk.

*

On visit days Mr Senshall opens the crypt, supervises the visitors' descent of the uneven stone steps, takes his stand by the shelves and announces, 'Welcome to my Underworld. Please move along into the space opposite the shelves, there is room for you all to see.' For the visitors, precious daylight fans across the floor and gradually diminishes in strength as it climbs the walls and recedes into darkness. As the visitors adjust to the gloom, chill and spectacle, they see that the walls are mottled grey clay, and bleached white skulls are ranged on racks of shelves that disappear into the furthest corners.

Obediently, the visitors shuffle along, mesmerised by the skulls and by Mr Senshall. With an officer's gaze he inspects them, standing a little forward of his parade, and lectures on the rigours of a pilgrim's life of poverty and the road. 'By making this sacrifice, by suffering to atone for their sins and the sins of others, the pilgrims invoked God's mercy to preserve life and civilised society in a time of plague and war.'

Transfixed by the pale heads, all the dead and the one living, the visitors submit to the reproach. When someone blenches or shivers, chastened out of their complacency, Mr Senshall glows with satisfaction: a troop of modern lives is no match for a legion of the fiercely pious.

According to how the day has gone, Mr Senshall engages with the skulls in his necropolis. This day he celebrates their joint triumph over the visitors, musing on the shells of calcified bone, each representing a life once lived that now gazes back through empty eye sockets at the new world in incredulity. Can a skull retain a residue of spirit? Could there be one skull from a more recent time?

*

For Ros, the day ended the same as usual. After collecting the children, sorting their meals, then finally getting them to bed, Thomas alternated between calling out, 'Story! I want a story,' and telling Henry, 'Dad lives with his mum now. I look after you. Behave when I tell you.'

Ros yelled, 'Thomas, I've had enough for one day,

for the last time go to sleep!'

Thomas hugged Henry and gave him a kiss before falling asleep.

*

No church council member had expressed concerns about Mr Senshall or his care of the crypt; they understood that he took every necessary action to preserve the collection for future generations and would brook no interference. But for each generation there comes an end.

'I hear the old boy was in there at midnight when it happened, talking to the dead,' said one local to another down at the Anchor.

Mr Senshall was found slumped against a shelf staring into a skull.

Was there a welcome to their underworld for him?

Runes of the Museum
by Alan Pattison

As usual, David had enjoyed his morning at the Victoria and Albert Museum. Even though he had visited many times, he nearly always found something new and interesting to see. This time the special exhibition of clothes from pre-Phoenician Egypt alone had made the trip worth the effort, and wandering through a few of the other galleries was a bonus.

Walking slowly up the road towards the park and the Albert Hall, he weighed up his options for what to do next. On a lovely spring day such as this, what could be nicer than a stroll through the park – or parks if he made it all the way to Marble Arch? However, he decided that he would try Kensington Church Street for a change and visit one or two antiques shops on the way.

In the first shop his eye was immediately drawn to a table with a variety of cutlery laid out. The bright silver set off the muted blue tablecloth beautifully and David could see that this was mostly serious antique silver, no doubt with very serious price tags attached. But, just as he was turning away, one scattered set of knives, forks and spoons caught his attention, as the design looked like it would be an excellent fit with his existing silver table pieces. The whole table setting would look perfect in their new house in Stoke Newington – he and his wife had just moved there, after getting married. He was sure that, once she had seen them, Jane would agree. He picked up a matching knife and fork, aware of a strange sensation coming over him as he did so, and turned towards the salesman he could sense was coming his way.

'Where do these come from?' he asked.

'Good choice, sir,' was the enthusiastic response. 'They are by William Hall. He is very popular now, especially as Prince George has taken a shine to his designs.'

David thought this a bit strange as he reckoned that Prince George was a bit young for silver, but then you could never quite tell with the Royal Family.

'That sounds perfect,' he said. 'How much are they?'

'For you, sir, four per setting. It's a reasonable price, as I'm sure you'll agree. May I ask how many settings sir would require?'

This surprised David, as he expected antique cutlery to be sold by the piece. Taking the salesman in for the first time, David was taken aback by his appearance: his coat and the rough clothes underneath looked more like what an old warehouseman might wear. But he seemed to know his stuff, and was looking at David quite anxiously.

'I will need to check when I get home; six should be enough, but perhaps eight. It depends on how many people my wife will invite to dinner! How soon could I have them?'

'And where does sir live?'

David put his hand in his pocket and pulled out his business cards. Just as he handed one over, his eye was caught by the address at the bottom, which stated that he lived in Cambridge Terrace. He was sure he'd checked these when he got them back from the printer after moving house. Cambridge Terrace was in Regent's Park, not Stoke Newington.

'Thank you, sir,' said the man, and looked closely at the card. 'In that case I can do them for three and six per setting, including delivery, and we should be able to get them to you within four weeks – unless you tell me that Prince George is coming round and you need them quicker!'

Something strange was definitely going on. Perhaps this Prince George was older and more important. The only other Prince George he knew of was the Prince Regent, later George IV. But that was a long time ago. Was this some kind of historical shop where they dressed and acted according to the period of the antiques they sold?

'No, sorry, wait, that's the wrong address,' David said, feeling confused. He didn't feel at all comfortable, and decided not to commit to a purchase before he understood what was going on. He wanted to go home – to Stoke Newington, not Regent's Park.

He said, 'I'll let you know as soon as I can. Thanks for all your help.'

'Goodbye, sir. You're welcome back any time, especially if you want to order that lovely cutlery. And do recommend us to a friend or two of yours.'

He went out the door, feeling a sense of relief as he got into the fresh air. He looked up the road. Everything looked much as it normally did – no horses or carriages, or Regency period outfits. As he walked towards the station he saw cars, and he was nearly bumped into by a young man shouting into his mobile phone. Grateful for once for twenty-first century behaviours, David wondered if he'd been hallucinating. Nothing had seemed strange when he entered the shop; what had happened?

It was the cutlery – as soon as he'd picked it up he seemed to enter a time-warp. A funny feeling came over him as he realised this was not the first time something like this had happened: he'd distinctly heard the sounds of the Roaring Twenties when he'd picked up an Art Deco vase in a charity shop just the other week.

An excited chill came over him as it dawned on him that he might possibly have the power to twist time. He checked his watch: there was just about time to check out another antiques shop before Jane would expect him home. He'd have to choose carefully what to pick up.

Poetry

On Looking at a Toy Soldier in the National Museum of Hungary
by Margaret Gallop

I was a soldier strong and bold
It was a way to earn my bread
by doing just as I was told.

I found my independence sold.
Now I make soldiers out of lead
I make them look both strong and bold.

They don't shed blood, they're metal, cold.
When shot they do not fall down dead
for doing just as they were told.

The model soldiers that I mould
will never lose their heart or head
unlike a soldier strong and bold.

The models which I sell for gold
have quite untroubled lives instead
and do not listen when they're told.

An altered credo I now hold.
Unlike my models I am wed,
a different heroism, bold,
and never doing what I'm told.

Gallery 624

by Susan G Duncan

The Altamira family reunited:
Father Vicente, mother Maria Ignacia,
sons Manuel and Vicente junior,
baby Augustina.

They're wearing their court finery:
silk and velvet and pearls.
Three-year-old Manuel sports a crimson jumpsuit,
ivory lace cups his dimpled chin,
ivory satin ties his waist and slippers.

Maria, fond of parties and card games,
drapes herself in rosy satin on a teal velvet couch,
balances her tiny daughter on her lap
and together they hold a nosegay of violets –
symbol of humility and modesty –
their vapid faces mirror images.

The heir and namesake and miniature of his father,
Vicente, ten,
is clad in diamond-studded copper,
a tiny wig, a tiny sword.
His little left fist, too, hides

aristocratically in his waistcoat,
just like his sire's.

But his nobleman father's not much taller –
the least man I ever saw in society,
an Englishman remarked –
and despite the gold thread embroidered
at chest cuffs knees and toes,
despite his many titles and his full name:
Vicente Joaquin Osorio de Moscoso y Guzman Fernandez
de Cordoba
there's no disguising his stature

and he's less than life-size here at the Met –
where guests visit in ball caps and sandals,
the parquet is scuffed,
the walls are bare

but for these five portraits
and the undeniable fact:
they're forgotten sitters in history
and Goya, the court painter, is not.

First published in *Constellations: A Journal of Poetry and Fiction*.

Upstairs in the Museum
by Maia Cornish

I met you last night
for the first time,
upstairs in the museum.
Towering above me,
you drew me into
your hidden folds and channels.
Your body shapes
were familiar, organic;
caves and crevices,
places to ponder.

I dressed your hair
and traced the hidden hoops
of your construction
with my eye.
I wanted
to tip you over
to see how you were made,
to take you outside
to see your colours
in natural light.

If I took you home
and placed you
by my window
would I find a name
for those shades,
woven and knotted
in tones of
trees,
plants,
and earth?

Next morning
you filled my mind
with your sweet scent
of soil and hemp,
caught in my clothes
like the lingering perfume
of a new lover,
and I knew I must
meet you again,
upstairs in the museum.

Dedicated to the hemp sculptures by Mrinalini Mukherjee
(1949-2015), Museum of Modern Art, Oxford, 1994.

In and Around Athens
by Janet McCann

So little left: a horse's bronzed shoe,
A head, an arm, a marble torso
In energetic action, arm upraised,

And the omphalos, the old one outside
Near the temple of Apollo, the new one
Here in the clean but sparsely-filled museum,

The great navel, the middle of the world.
And you can touch it, put your palm
Over its curve, it looks like a rocket.

Under Thebes is buried the old Thebes,
The real Thebes. The guide tells the story
Of Oedipus, as though it was all blunt fact,

As though you could go out and interview
Oedipus' great great grandchild, through Ismene's
Line, of course, and pick up another angle.

There on your left, the bus driver tells us,
You see the very crossroads where Oedipus
Slew his father Laius, you can see

Where Laius came up on the right – our necks
Symmetrically crane, we look out into the valley,
Happy enough to think about the city, the real city,

Under the diminished world, to believe
Somehow the past supports us. *You just have*
To use your imagination, says the guide.

The Small Philosopher
by Laura Connochie

Vaulted ceilings whalebone over exotic minutiae;
the big bang documented in orderly rows –
custodians of the ages, the length of time it would take
to see everything. A stuffed Shetland pony,
fur turned to corduroy from children's fingers
and now mine: a taxidermist's playground.

Look through the skeleton belly of an African elephant
read that their lives are only as long as their six teeth
before they starve. But elephants are tender
and have memory, and often visit the bones of loved ones.

The Oxford dodo shakes his carnival costume
flat feet and pointed beaky smile,
oblivious to his singularity.

Glass cabinets, dark wooden specimen drawers,
tables of fossiliferous treasures, dinosaur teeth,
Japanese spider crabs, a baby Nile crocodile,
live cockroaches' rich clicking and bottom-crawling,
pinprick gleam of giant crystals – too much –
just too much.

Now old school polished parquet footsteps ring
from chimp to man: increasing brain volume,
decreasing lower jaw –
the hairy eureka when an avant-garde ape
stretched and stood up for good. In the last cabinet
a human skeleton, yellow and grinning,
sat down, posed, a Rodin in-joke.

A small boy, five or six, lays sticky palms
against the glass and eagerly asks his dad,
'Is he dead?' Glee in his high voice.
'Well, he's a skeleton.'
'Yes, but is he dead?'
'OK, for you he's dead.'
Pause.
The *Tyrannosaurus rex* across the hall awaits.
Millions of years of evolution condensed into
this single six-year-old *Homo sapiens*' verdict:
'Oh well – everyone dies one day!'
Skeleton solved, he lightly moves
to the next display. Dad rolls his eyes at me
and I smile, but the lesson rings in my ears
and we are put in our place.

You and I
by Gigi Bassi

What am I, exactly?
a vision,
a dream,
an enchanted window
to a world they escape to?

They search me,
I search them,
faces replacing faces,
yet they all share one thing:
a yearning
to be understood,
to belong.

Oh, how I recognise,
waiting
to be touched
from the depths of your soul,
to feel enlightened,
special,
to feel more than just ordinary,
to feel more then an everyday museum piece.

I stare deep into their essence,
as they stand and stare at my strokes and blobs
That they thoughtlessly call art.

For, every time,
they fail to see themselves,
for the art that's in this room
is in them all along.
– how they search meaning and beauty in me,
when it's all in them.

I show them this
and they smile,
a smile
that I could never hold,
yet they wish to be part of my world.

The Museum,
a place,
a universal home,
where time flows in strange ways,
where paintings like me and you
sit and wait
on opposite sides for the big wide doors
to finally open,

and there it is,
art,
oh, so beautiful –
they come in,
so full of colour,
so full of light,
magic,
dancing in the spaces between you and me.

Tell me your stories,
and I will show you my worlds,
for you and I both know
it's the one time
we feel alive.

Self-Realisation at the Library of Congress

by Karla Linn Merrifield

Though no longer on the map,
you were always more than
Terra Incognito quilled
in a cartographer's calligraphy
in mid-ocean between continents Old and New.

You were the name for who I am:
woman, ergo, of inner vastness unknown.

Dutch Realism, Rijksmuseum
by Janet Bowdan

We're given the children's tour, a booklet of clues
Noah's following eagerly from room to room,
finding the complicated clock mechanism,
the Delft blue and white cow, the filigreed armour,
the Avercamp scene of winter skaters including
the one who's tumbled on his behind, just like Noah
the last time we tried to get him on the ice.
When we put the clues together, we'll have letters
we can arrange to form a secret password
Noah will whisper to the woman in the gift shop
for his prize, so he's in a hurry, tugging as I pause
to look at Pieter De Hooch's *A Mother's Duty*:
her child is kneeling on the floor inside, head in her lap
as she carefully parts his hair with her hands, looking
for nits. 'The act of combing is a reference
to the cleansing of the soul,' the audio-tour guide said,
'which is also a mother's duty.' I won't need to check
my little guy for nits (ick, and ick) for several years
so I don't realise then that De Hooch has it wrong,
putting mother and child next to the bed in the dark
interior of the house while light spills onto the mother
through a high window and again through the half door
in the outer room at the left of the scene. How can she see
anything? The light should be on the child, they should

both be in the outer room, in the light, and the cat,
who for some reason is in the dark foreground just gazing
at the patch of sun, should be there too, getting underfoot
for verisimilitude. I thought, then, that I had
everything to learn, and I was right. Noah tugged
and we went on, following him.

Next Life at the Museum
by Cynthia Gallaher

Have the living anywhere to sit in this museum?
– dedicated this season to the Day of the Dead,
el Dia de los Muertos.

A couple makes out on the end
of the only available bench,
full tilt boogie in the south gallery.

He sits, she stands like a Katrina,
his pants striped like a love prisoner,
she engulfs him.

I sit on the far end, face the other way,
open my notebook,
the walls of the museum dissolve to

my German-Irish stepfather John
who used to play basketball here everyday,
perhaps his footfalls crossed the very spot where I sit

when the building was the Harrison Park Fieldhouse,
before it transformed into the
National Museum of Mexican Art.

His father ran a tavern down on
Cullerton Avenue, where John helped
make 'french-fried potatoes' for customers.

But, after each sweaty basketball practice or game,
park district showers pounded his head
until he started losing hair

which grew back from black to ghost white
at age thirty, remaining full and thick
until the day he died.

He passed into the next world,
this museum an invisible ofrenda to him
that only I know about.

Now a sacred place for Mexicans
to honour their own dead
each November.

The Harrison Park Fieldhouse
passed, too,
into the next world,

or rather just around the corner
where they rebuilt it,
long and modern and new.

Beloved and caring stepfather John,
where is your new life?
Is it celestial or reincarnated?

Maybe you are here, in this museum,
as the young Chicano artist
contemplating the altar he just installed,

dedicated to those gone, or gone too soon,
surrounded in marigolds,
pan de muerte, bowls of fruits,

unlit candles, old trophies,
sugar skulls, paper streamers,
all perishables, like your life, like mine,

while showers of light
continue to pour down from
vast Raya and Romero murals

over our heads.

Museum of my Mind
by Claire Selby

To some, full, to others, empty.
The first galleries fly past in a swirl of images and
    film clips:
Laughter, shock, leaves in flickering sunlight;
Dark shadows, empty spaces flashed with nightmare
    faces.

Wander over here and you find a wealth of energy
    and knowledge,
Brush against a hilarious tale of the time when….
Stop short at the threshold of a grey-black void
Echoing with nothing, but hung with fraying strands
    of loosely fixed information
Blown about by a changeable wind.

Years stretch back to the basement and, fading,
    disappear.
You call out and a picture, glazed in age and event
Trundles up in the dumbwaiter, to be served
Each time with a new garnish.

Above, the freshly painted rooms are waiting.
What will you make to store here?
How many visitors will break their day to hurry in?
How many hurry out?

What special exhibition can you draw from the past
And make relevant today?
Reveal your self in juxtaposed contrasts
For private viewings only, or public gaze?

Digital words hover insubstantial on a shimmer of
    electrons,
As fragile as memory.
More easily shattered than ancient shards.

Store or display? The writer curates.
Each interconnected fragment is precious.
In a museum of the mind, how can you choose?

Twilight Zone at the Holocaust Museum

by Janet Bowdan

I'm telling myself it's not like that episode,
Nobody's been replaced at the height of their
    popularity,
Led to a secret cell while their eternally good-looking
Image takes over their job, the public never
    suspecting.
The survivors, aged and fragile, are still here,
Their holograms made to ensure that the truth
They witnessed can be told no matter what.
The truth has substance though: you can reach out a
    hand
And it will touch nothing, or light. It will touch light.

We've lost so much. We've lost so many
Led to secret cells, replaced in their youth,
All that brilliant potential. Let's just take a moment
To grieve for whole families, entire villages
Erased, their existence plastered over with denial.
We remember best those who had at least one escape
To safety, stories of the parents who sent their child
Told by that child, now old, and his hologram
In the museum, where you can reach out a hand
Through the image, this light surviving.

Museum
by Alex Phuong

Physical buildings

And artistic architecture

Holding remnants from the past.

Museums hold artifacts

Yet artistic expression,

Hope

And creativity

Pave the way for the future.

This present moment in time

Is the greatest gift of all

Because it is, thankfully, not the last.

The Money Museum in Athens
by Janet McCann

The coins are the clearest record.
The old Greek faces. The Aegean lips,
Is that scorn or sadness? I can't tell.

The guide says they were sad
Because their age was ending.
But the high curved philtrum looks like scorn.

Arethusa or Persephone with dolphins,
Turtle, symbol of what? And all those men.
Case after case of them, since the seventh century

BC or maybe earlier, but it is
too hot – we enter the movie room
where in the humid dark hands pass coins

and bills for love or hatred or desire,
ambition or rage, every film transaction –
fat hands and thin, warty, smooth, all colours –

frozen, abstracted from everything it
ever meant, like a coin in a case.

Hat Museum, Stockport
by Janet Bowdan

No sooner have I got off the train
with a hug from my exuberant aunt Ruth
than she whisks me off to the hat museum,
factory on the outside, seventeenth-century inside,
not even a cup of tea first, but a vat of
animal hairs being stirred together, wool
probably, a display of wet felting,
the liquid (did they really say urine?)
pressed out and fashioned into grey cones
recognisably a sort of hat, leading
into the next process, mercuric nitrate
making rabbit pelts toxic to the hatters
as they blocked the felt from the fur.
A cheerful advertisement
tells us, 'If you want to get ahead...
get a hat!' Ruth propels us out on her itinerary:
the Jewish Museum where she docented
and wants me to see Grandma's dishes loaned
to the Jews in Baghdad exhibit, and tomorrow
either Lyme Park (where she docents) or
Mrs Gaskell's (where she docents) with
a running commentary on the age of the windows,
the one black building in Manchester,
the peppered moth – until all times, artifacts

and archives jumble in my head together
with how she'd prepare pills back in the '6os
when she was a pharmacist, mixing ingredients
and rolling them into little balls not at all like
pre-made tablets some machine of crushed powder
compresses and spits into a plastic bottle.
Ruth is my favorite museum, full
of exhibits even if some visitors disagree with
her version of events (my mother, for one) and
even if I leave awed and wondering what to do
with all that information, I always want to go back.

Cartography
by MJ Moore

Lamplight and shadow patrol the mind's museum.
Guide and tourists drift down the corridor,
recede and vanish.

Unseen, alone, I wander an ancient atlas,
trace caravan routes, sway with camels
laden with brilliant brocade, spicy perfume.
Along the Silk Road at Samarkand
I pause to dip my ladle in a surging spring.
Mountains stretch against scarred desert.
Cloaked in goat skin,
I trudge through snowbound passes,
hunt white fox and hare.

At the center of the hall
indigo globes slowly spin,
circled in golden stars.
Constellations of primal light.

On fading frescoes distant battles rage.
Cannon fire flashes
as ships lay siege to fortified cities.
In open water Poseidon whips
his horse to a white froth
while all around
fantastic creatures writhe.
The topography of dreams,
charted but not travelled.

Yes, the old ones knew,
Here be dragons.

Carpe Diem
by Sheila Davie

Who am I?
Not a relic of the past
Nor a vision of the future.
I am invisible
As I wander through the museum
Of life,
Touching, hearing,
Seeing, smelling,
feeling
like an outsider
Confused
Alone

Yet I sense a glimmer of hope
A light
In the darkness
Pulling me upwards,
Lifting my spirits,
Calming my fears.
Mindful, in that moment,

I banish all thoughts
Of doom and gloom
For I am now:
This is my time
To show who I am,
To speak my voice

I float on a cloud:
The fog has lifted,
The earth spins.
Darkness and light –
Mirrors reflect
The museum of life.
This is me,
We are one.

Palazzo Piccolomini
by Janet McCann

Fifteenth century in movies: all that
colour and noise, no feel to it,
steaming indefinite meals
out of focus and paintings
you can't quite see, just a whirl of
fabrics and fighting. Fifteenth century
in museums: labelled cases, guide
with a bright umbrella telling
the same half-truths, knowing
nothing beyond. Any questions?
Now let's move on to the statues.
and then this place – the gardens,
carved boxwoods and roses
behind hedges and great marble
bird baths and green alleys. The
rooms with a few of their belongings:
wooden chests and a four-poster
bed, its last guest was in 1960.
Fabric a little faded but still
lustrous with the sheen of time,
you place your hand on it,
look at the blue veins, the pulse,
feeling the truth of time.

Museum Piece
by Paula Bonnell

Homage to Frank O'Hara

1

I leave the office at 5:5o
and find free parking near the MFA.
The ficus in the lobby
has eight trunks,
but because three of them
split, it seems Japanese.
I drink washing-machine beer (two)
and eat rich-people's food:
almost no mesclun greens,
almost no goat cheese,
with two big slabs of tomato,
yellow and red.

2

I don't know whether
to be happy or sad
for Nina (1935-1991)
in whose memory
an elevator

3

When I look at the twentieth-century works
I pay close attention
to the year they were born.
Are they older or younger
than me?
(Their pants were tighter.)

4

I emerge – it is Magritte twilight.
The gates to the Japanese garden,
one in a series of planes:
  curly, dense, night-lit shrubbery,
      the bulge of a grainy stone lantern,
          the flat bleached greys of the gates
              (with
              and without the Pru
      against the dark sky behind)
are a work by me
(1945-)

About the Authors

Jane Andrews is a museum aficionado who likes writing about human relationships. She belongs to the Birmingham Writers' Group.

Gigi Bassi is from the West Midlands. She enjoys pondering and observing life's beauty, and reflecting this in her poetry. She is part of the West Bromwich writers' group.

Charles Bonkowsky: Writer and student from Utah (USA), interested in all things speculative fiction.

Paula Bonnell's *Airs & Voices* won the Ciardi prize; her poems have appeared widely and in three other collections.

Janet Bowdan's poems have appeared in *Denver Quarterly*, *Isthmus*, *Blood Orange Review*, and elsewhere. She lives in Northampton, Massachusetts.

Daren Carpmail: I'm a fifty-one-year-old writer from the West Midlands. I got into writing several years ago as part of an ongoing midlife crisis.

Laura Connochie, aka amusenut, is originally from Cornwall but is now based in Didcot. Her confessional poetry aims to observe life and express beauty.

Noa Covo is a sixteen-year-old student. Her writing will appear in the literary magazine *5x5*. She lives in Tel Aviv, Israel.

Maia Cornish began writing when she retired. Born in Cornwall, her extensive travels have inspired her short stories and poems.

Sheila Davie enjoys the challenge of writing competitions and is trying out poetry as a means of conveying emotions within a given theme.

Lal Dhillon is a writer, musician and student of theology based in Glasgow, Scotland.

Susan G Duncan: I consult with arts clients, capping executive roles with California Shakespeare Theater and Grammy-winning Chanticleer. My poetry appears in thirty-plus journals.

Adele Evershed currently lives in the USA where the lack of urgency about the climate emergency chills her!

Mike Evis lives in Abingdon, Oxfordshire. He has always been interested in writing, and his stories have appeared in a number of anthologies.

Tessa Fenley has just finalised her first detective novel. She lives by the sea, which invariably inspires her work.

Cynthia Gallaher, a Chicago-based poet, is author of four poetry collections, including *Epicurean Ecstasy: More Poems About Food, Drink, Herbs and Spices*.

Margaret Gallop: I enjoyed teaching Oxfordshire children creative writing and am now experimenting with poetry and short story writing for myself.

Jody Kish has nine stories published online, and is gracious for the recognition of each one as she continues to learn the craft.

Alice Little currently has seventeen short stories in print and online, in addition to having published four anthologies. See alicelittle.co.uk/fiction for more information, and follow her on Twitter and Instagram at @littleamiss.

Rose Little: It's a great pleasure to sit in the garden, watched over by my cat, running scenes and characters through my mind, always hoping that others will enjoy them too. Belonging to Didcot Writers has been a great encouragement.

John Ludlam: Besides a career in IT I have squeezed in reading from Aeschylus to Zadie Smith. Now to write.

Janet McCann: I'm a Texas crone poet who taught Creative Writing at Texas A&M University for forty-six years.

Karla Linn Merrifield's newest of fourteen books is her full-length *Athabaskan Fractal: Poems of the Far North* from Cirque Press.

MJ Moore lives in the San Francisco Bay Area. Various incarnations have included technical editor, environmental activist, teacher, and poet.

Charles Osborne has had poetry and prose published in several small-press magazines.

Alan Pattison: a semi-retired researcher of local history.

Alex Phuong graduated from California State University, Los Angeles with his Bachelor of Arts in

English in 2015.

David Lewis Pogson: Fiction writer for ACES *The Terrier* magazine. Winner – Cumbria Local History Federation Prize, Freerange Theatre Playframe, and MicrcosmsFic. www.davidlewispogson.wordpress.com

Georgina Richardson is a primary teacher and mum of two boys. She lives in Yorkshire and writes in her spare time.

Claire Selby: I write English learning materials using specific, limited vocabulary (twenty years). It's fun to use extra words now and again! www.claireselby.org

Lee Shupe: I am a middle school teacher who thinks too much about art theft.

Marsha Webb: I am currently a full time teacher but have started writing recently, I have had a number of short stories published and my first novella, *You can choose your sin...but you cannot choose the consequences*, was published in 2019.

Other Books

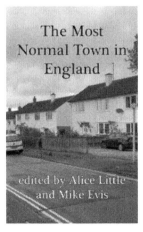

The Most Normal Town in England
In this anthology authors were challenged to consider what makes a town normal – or not: who lives there, who never leaves, what skeletons are lurking in the closets? From sci-fi to romance, from horror to literary fiction, this book contains 42 stories by 40 authors detailing the happenings in a range of apparently normal English towns, villages and cities.

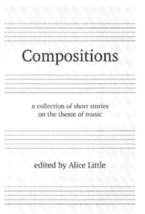

Compositions: a collection of short stories on the theme of music
The stories in this book were selected from among the submissions to Didcot Writers' summer competition 2018. You can read some of the stories online at didcotwriters.wordpress.com, where you can also find out about new opportunities.

From musicians to collectors, instruments to electronics, this book approaches the theme of music from a range of directions.

First Contact
This anthology was published in September 2019, and features thirty-one stories from thirty authors from Didcot and beyond, in a range of genres and styles. From meeting a stranger in 1970s Africa to adopting a child, from a mass hallucination to making contact with criminals – this book considers first encounters and new beginnings – and what happens next.

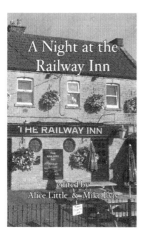

A Night at the Railway Inn
The pub has stood across the road from the station ever since the railway was built... In this anthology, sixteen authors take us inside the Railway Inn, introduce us to its landlords and regulars, and let us eavesdrop on some of the conversations at the bar. From beer and karaoke to ghosts and spies - crossing genres from crime thriller to comedy - this apparently workaday pub has a number of surprises in store for those who step through its doors.